ERIN BROCKOVICH

SCREENPLAY
AND INTRODUCTION WRITTEN BY
SUSANNAH GRANT

THE NHB SHOOTING SCRIPT SERIES

NICK HERN BOOKS
LONDON
www.nickhernbooks.co.uk

The Shooting Script Series

This book first published in Great Britain in 2001
by Nick Hern Books Limited, 14 Larden Road, London W3 7ST

A CIP catalogue record for this book is available from the British Library

ISBN 1 85459 633 0

Printed and bound in Great Britain by Hobbs the Printers Ltd,
Totton, Hants. SO40 3YS

THE NHB SHOOTING SCRIPT SERIES
I Went Down
The Ice Storm
Saltwater
The Shawshank Redemption
The Truman Show

For information on forthcoming titles, please contact the publishers:
NHB, 14 Larden Road, London W3 7ST

CONTENTS

Introduction iv

The Screenplay 1

Stills 114

Production Notes 121

Credits 131

INTRODUCTION

BY SUSANNAH GRANT

If you've bought this book—or even if you're just thumbing through it in a bookstore—you probably have at least a passing interest in screenwriting. Which means you probably know of the Screenwriter's Lament. On any given night, you can hear this cry echoing through the canyons of the Hollywood Hills. It goes something like this: "THEY'VE RUINED IT!" You see, there are three sure things in a screenwriter's life: the sun will rise in the morning; the Red Sox will not win the World Series; and, if you write a script you love, someone somewhere will come along and destroy it.

In 1997, I wrote a script I loved. Early in that year, I'd had the amazing good fortune to meet a woman named Erin Brockovich. I was introduced to her through the folks at Jersey Pictures, who had optioned the movie rights to her story and needed someone to write the script. Erin had writer approval, so a lunch was arranged for the two of us. We met at Café Med, on the Sunset Strip (I was wearing jeans and a sweater. Erin was wearing a leather bustier and four-inch pumps.). I remember the two of us initially being the polite, nice-firm-handshake, pleased-to-meet-you gals we both were brought up to be. But within ten minutes, we found ourselves laughing so hard we couldn't speak, and spewing enough four-letter words to make our handsome Greek waiter turn crimson.

So Erin, bless her heart, approved of me, and I set about trying to turn a huge, complicated five-year chunk of her life and work into 120 pages of cohesive screenplay. The question I'm asked most often about this movie is how much of it is true. And my answer is, it's almost entirely true, but it's not the whole truth. Any life is complex, and Erin's, especially in the years of the PG&E trial, was labyrinthine. Writing the script was a matter of figuring out which parts of that labyrinth were essential to the story I was telling;

which were germane; which were expendable; and which were inessential, but so damn funny, you couldn't possibly leave them out.

I holed up in my office and, several months later, emerged with a finished first draft. And let me tell you—handing a fresh first draft over to anyone is a nerve-wracking experience, but I promise you, nothing compares to the anxiety that comes with giving it to the person on whom it is based. The silence of my phone while I waited for Erin's reaction was one of the most deafening sounds I can remember. I don't know how long it took her to get back to me—it felt like a month and a half; it was probably two days. Then I came home one day and saw that little light blinking on my machine. There had been an exchange in that draft of the script (which didn't make it into the movie) in which one of Erin's co-workers gives her a hard time about how short her skirt is. The co-worker says, "Erin, for God's sakes, I can see your panties," and Erin says back, "Liar. I'm not wearing any." So I pressed the button on my answering machine, and out came Erin's voice, deep and low, saying, "I *always* wear panties."

It's a very risky thing, letting someone turn your life into a feature film. Sure, you could come across well, like Bob Woodward in *All The President's Men*, but then again, you could just as easily end up looking like Joan Crawford in *Mommie Dearest*. To her immense credit, Erin wasn't vain; she wasn't paranoid; she didn't suffer about how she would appear, or who would play her, or whether she'd be likeable. In fact, she didn't really care. She said to me, more than once, that even if she came across badly, it would be worth it, as long as the world found out what PG&E did to those people in Hinkley.

So I had finished the script. Enter the Screenwriter's Lament. I'd written something I loved; ergo, someone would come along to destroy it. The only question was who. I decided it was going to be the actress. See, I was convinced that that we could never, ever find an actress who could come close to capturing Erin's vitality, her complexity, her fascinating mix of fun and seriousness, frivolity and astonishing depth. Plus, she had to be a knock-out. Impossible. Doesn't exist.

And then I heard that Julia Roberts was going to do the part. Now, as the entire universe knows, Julia Roberts is nothing if not vital, complex, with a fascinating mix of fun and seriousness, frivolity and astonishing depth. Plus, she's a knock-out. There went that theory.

Okay, fine, I said to myself, they may have the perfect actress. But a brilliant performance is worthless if it isn't supported by a good movie. And for that you need a good director. No, not a good director, a great director. Someone who can have fun with the laughs without turning them into broad comedy. Someone who can be honest and moving with the emotional moments of the script without turning them into melodrama. Someone who can direct the movie with a style that will elevate the material without overwhelming it. Impossible, I said. Doesn't exist.

Enter Steven Soderbergh. A great director. Possibly the best director working in this business now. Try as I might to find something somewhere in his body of work that would support my theory that he was the one who was going to destroy my script, I couldn't.

As time went on, in fact, I found it frustratingly impossible to find anyone on whom I could hang that burden. The producers at Jersey are famously good at protecting material and bringing out the best in it. The studio, Universal, was nothing but supportive. The costume designer, Jeffrey Kurland, captured Erin's style perfectly. The crew wrapped early, and under budget. And on and on. Slowly, gradually, the incredible truth sank in: nobody was destroying the script I loved. They were changing it a little, yes—tweaking here, shifting there, adding this, taking that out—but it was only getting better and better.

We tested the movie in Sacramento in the fall of '99. It scored through the roof. There were virtually no negative comments on the little cards that the audience turns. Or actually, there was one. One person—an older man, I think—wrote: "The hundredth time I saw Julia Roberts's breasts was too many. But one through ninety-nine were fantastic."

I love the script I wrote for *Erin Brockovich*. But even more, I love the movie. I love what it started as, and I love everything that was added to it by all the bright, talented people who came onto the project after me. If you get half as much enjoyment from reading it as I did from writing it, it will be time well spent.

SUSANNAH GRANT also wrote the screenplays for *28 Days*, a feature about drug and alcohol rehab, starring Sandra Bullock; co-wrote *Ever After*, starring Drew Barrymore; and co-wrote *Pocahontas*, the 1995 Disney animated feature. She was also a writer/producer/director for three seasons on the popular series *Party of Five*. She was the recipient of the prestigious 1992 Nicholl Fellowship in Screenwriting from the Academy of Motion Picture Arts and Sciences.

ERIN BROCKOVICH

Written by

Susannah Grant

FADE IN:

INT. DR. JAFFE'S OFFICE - DAY.

A successful-looking doctor sits behind a desk in a well-appointed office. He's looking at someone off-camera.

> DR. JAFFE
> ...Uh, but you have no actual medical training?

> ERIN
> (off)
> No. I have kids. Learned a lot right there. I've seen nurses give my son a throat culture. I mean what is it - you stick a giant Q-tip down their throat and wait. Or a urine analysis, with that dipstick that tells you whether or not the white count is high...

> DR. JAFFE
> Yes, I understand.

> ERIN
> (off)
> And, I mean, I'm great with people. Of course, you'd have to observe me to know for sure, but trust me on that one. I'm extremely fast learner. I mean, you show me what to do in a lab once, and I've got it down.

He nods. Now we see who he is talking to: ERIN BROCKOVICH. How to describe her? A beauty queen would come to mind - which, in fact, she was. Tall in a mini skirt, legs crossed, tight top, beautiful - but clearly from a social class and geographic orientation whose standards for displaying beauty are not based on subtlety. She can sense she's losing him, as he scans her "resume";

> ERIN (cont'd)
> ... But see, I had always wanted to go to medical school. That was my first interest really...but then I, you know, got married..had a kid too young and..that kind of blew it for me....When I was first out of high school, I was working at Fleuer Engineers and Constructors in Irvine. I fell madly in love with geology.

> DR. JAFFE
> Geology?

(CONTINUED)

                         ERIN
          Yeah, I learned how to read maps. I love
          maps...But I lost that job because my son
          came down with the Chicken Pox and 104
          temperature and my ex-husband was useless,
          so..yah know...

Jaffe just stares at her.

                         DR. JAFFE
          Uh-huh.

                         ERIN
                  (beat, looks around)
          This is a really nice office.

Jaffe looks down at her resume, trying to figure a polite
route.

                         DR. JAFFE
          Thanks.
                  (looks up at her)
          Look....

Beat. By Erin's expression, she knows what's coming.

EXT. DR. JAFFE'S OFFICE / SO. CALIFORNIA SUBURB, MAIN DRAG - DAY

A side street. No pedestrians, just parked cars.

Erin is finishing a cigarette. Her face has fallen -- the
enthusiasm and spirit she showed in the interview are now
replaced by a desperate type of concern. She takes a final
puff, puts the cigarette out and walks to her car.

A PARKING TICKET flaps under the wiper of a an old Hyundai.

                         ERIN
          Fuck.

Even when she talks dirty, there's a heartland goodness to
her voice. Like Kansas corn fields swaying in the breeze.

She grabs the ticket from the windshield. As Erin starts to
open the driver's door, she breaks one of her fingernails on
the handle.

                         ERIN (cont'd)
          God _damn_ it.

She tends to the nail as she opens her car door and gets in.

WIDER ON THE STREET

                                                      (CONTINUED)

CONTINUED:

The Hyundai starts up, signals. Then, just as it pulls
slowly out into the street, a JAGUAR barrels around the
corner, accelerating out of the turn, and SLAMS into the side
of Erin's car, sending it CAREENING into the median. It
SMASHES into a foot-thick lamppost. And stops.

EXT. MASRY & VITITOE - RECEPTION - DAY

A sign over the reception desk reads: MASRY & VITITOE,
ATTORNEYS AT LAW.

ED MASRY, senior partner in the firm, enters the office. His
avuncular presence masks a savvy legal mind, and his somewhat
rumpled appearance indicates a disinterest in pretense.
ROSALIND, a middle-aged receptionist, sits behind the front
desk.

                    ROSALIND
          Good morning, Mr. Masry.

                    ED
          Good morning, Rosalind.

                    ROSALIND
          How are you doing today?

                    ED
          I'm fine, thanks. And you?

                    ROSALIND
          Very well. Thank you for asking.

INT. MASRY & VITITOE - MAIN ROOM - DAY

Ed walks across the busy office, greeting the office workers.
He approaches his secretary BRENDA's desk.

                    BRENDA
          Did you watch it last night?

                    ED
          No, I was out. I taped it. Don't tell me
          what happens.

                    BRENDA
                 (overlapping him,
                  excitedly)
          It's sooo great...
                 (as he walks to office)
          Your nine-o'clock's already in there.

Ed peers into his office. Standing in the middle of the room
is Erin, in a teensy, leopard-print mini-dress.

                                             (CONTINUED)

CONTINUED:

As she jiggles a spike-heeled foot, everything about her
shimmies gloriously. Except her head, which is held in place
by a neck brace.

> ED
> Remind me.

> BRENDA
> Erin Brockovich. Car accident. Not her
> fault, she says.
> > (beat. they exchange looks)
> She was referred.

> ED
> Oh.

> BRENDA
> Yeah.

> ED
> All right.

He nods.

INT. MASRY & VITITOE - ED'S OFFICE - DAY

Not an office that necessarily exudes authority, and Ed's
blustery entrance only adds to the sense of chaos.

> ED
> Erin -- Hi. Ed Masry. Sorry you had to
> wait. Here, sit down, sit down.

He clears a stack of papers off a chair, places down a mug of
coffee.

> ERIN
> Thanks a lot.
> > (as she sits)
> I tell you, I never thought just standing
> could take it out of you, but ever since
> that shithead hit me, I feel like my whole
> body's put together wrong.

Ed gives her a look full of pro-forma sympathy.

> ED
> > (sits)
> You poor thing. Did anyone ask if you want
> some coffee?

> ERIN
> Yeah. I'm fine.

CONTINUED:

                    ED
          Good. Well listen...whoever did this to
          you made one hell of a mistake, and you
          and me, we're gonna make him pay for it.

He sips coffee like it's a healing potion, takes out a pad
and paper, gets ready to write.

                    ED (cont'd)
          Why don't you tell me what happened?

                                        CUT TO:

INT. SOUTHERN CALIFORNIA COURTROOM - DAY

Erin is on the stand, wearing the most conservative thing she
owns: a red, form-fitting mini-dress, telling her story to
Ed, who's questioning her.

                    ERIN
          I was pulling out real slow, and out of
          nowhere, his Jaguar comes racing around
          the corner like a bat outta hell...

She glances at the defendant's table, where a DOCTOR sits
nobly. His WIFE and two beautiful KIDS are behind him. A
frigging Norman Rockwell painting.

LATER IN HER TESTIMONY

                    ERIN
          They took some bone from my hip and put it
          in my neck. I didn't have insurance, so
          I'm about seventeen thousand in debt right
          now.

STILL LATER

                    ERIN
          ...couldn't take painkillers 'cause they
          made me too groggy to take care of my
          kids.

STILL LATER

                    ERIN
          ...Matthew's eight, Katie's almost six,
          and Beth's just nine months.

STILL LATER

                                        (CONTINUED)

CONTINUED:

> ERIN
> ...just wanna be a good mom, a nice
> person, a decent citizen. Just wanna take
> good care of my kids. You know?

> ED
> (oh so moved)
> Yeah. I know.

INT. COURTROOM - LATER

Erin is still on the stand. But now the doctor's lawyer is
questioning her.

> DEFENDING LAWYER
> Seventeen thousand in debt. Whew. Is
> your ex-husband helping out?

> ERIN
> Which one?

> DEFENDING LAWYER
> (feigning shock)
> There's more than one?

> ERIN
> Yeah. There's two. Why?

Erin looks over at the jury. The personification of
conservative family values. Oh, shit.

STILL LATER

The defendant's lawyer is on the offensive. Erin's starting
to feel the case slipping away.

> DEFENDING LAWYER
> So. You must've been feeling pretty
> desperate that afternoon.

> ERIN
> (pointed)
> What's your point?

Ed shakes his head slightly to her -- don't get mad.

> DEFENDING LAWYER
> Broke, three kids, no job. A doctor in a
> Jaguar must've looked like a pretty good
> meal ticket.

Erin sees jurors nodding almost imperceptibly in agreement.
She's on a sinking ship.

(CONTINUED)

CONTINUED:

                    ED
          Objection.

                    JUDGE
          Sustained.

                    ERIN
          What? Hey -- he hit me.

                    DEFENDING LAWYER
          So you say.

                    ERIN
          He came tearing around the corner, out of
          control --

                    DEFENDING LAWYER
          An E.R. doctor who spends his days saving
          lives was the one out of control --

                    ERIN
                 (erupting)
          That asshole smashed in my fucking neck!

INT. COURTHOUSE CORRIDOR - LATER THAT DAY.

Erin barrels toward the elevator. Ed trails.

                    ERIN
          ...Open and shut? Open and fucking shut?

                    ED
          This is exactly the kind of language that
          lost the case.

                    ERIN
          Oh, please, it was over long before then.

                    ED
          I told you the questions might get a
          little persona--

                    ERIN
          No. You told me I'd be set.

Ed notices her ranting is starting to draw attention.

                    ED
          I didn't say that.

                    ERIN
          You told me I had a good shot! I had no
          shot!

(CONTINUED)

                         ED
          Okay -- let's try and settle down here,
          shall we?

                         ERIN
          Fuck settle down! I got seventy-four
          dollars to my name! I can't afford to
          settle down!

Beat.

                         ED
          I'm sorry, Erin.

                         ERIN
          Do they teach lawyers to apologize?
          Because you suck at it.

Erin turns away from him and heads for the stairway.

EXT. ERIN'S HOUSE - DAY

A shitty little house in a shitty part of Northridge. The
Hyundai with a bashed-in side pulls up to the curb.

Erin gets out, takes the mail from her mailbox, then heads
over to the equally grim house next door and rings the bell.

A Hispanic woman in her 60's opens the door, holding a white
baby. This is MRS. MORALES.

                         MRS. MORALES
          Hi, Erin! You're back so soon.

She hands Erin the baby. It's BETH, Erin's 9-month old.
Erin avoids the question by focusing on her baby.

                         ERIN
          Hi, sweetie. Were you a good girl?

The truth is too depressing to share. They walk towards
Erin's house as they talk...

                         ERIN (cont'd)
          You're my little baby.
                    (BETH COUGHS in
                     her arms)
          What is that? A little cough?

                         MRS. MORALES
          She's got a little cough. I sat with her
          in the steam to loosen it up. But...

                                                     (CONTINUED)

CONTINUED:

> ERIN
> I've got cough medicine I think..

> MRS. MORALES
> Ai, bueno. Listen, I didn't want to tell
> you before, with your worries --

> ERIN
> What?

> MRS. MORALES
> My daughter, she's bought a big house with
> a room for me. I'm going to move in with
> her.

> ERIN
> You're moving away? When?

> MRS. MORALES
> Next week.

> ERIN
> (stunned)
> Next week?

> MRS. MORALES
> I know. But it's good for me. Now I can
> help my daughter take care of my
> grandkids. And it's good for you too.
> Now you have money, you can find a good
> baby-sitter, huh? Not the old lady next
> door.

Oh, God. Beth COUGHS.

EXT. ERIN'S BACKYARD - DAY

Erin looks over the backyard fence. MATTHEW Erin's eight-
year-old son, and KATIE, her six-year-old daughter, play in a
water sprinkler.

> ERIN
> Hey, get in the house! No dripping!

INT. ERIN'S HOUSE - KITCHEN - DAY

Hand held camera follows Erin as she puts down her bag and
looks through the cabinets to see what she can make for
dinner, all the while holding Beth who coughs on and off.

(CONTINUED)

CONTINUED:

                    ERIN
          Oh sweetie..please don't get sick on
          me...my baby...let me just start
          dinner....

Erin finds nothing but boxes of macaroni and cheese and some
canned peaches and vegetables. She pulls out a box of
macaroni and cheese and a can of peas. She bends down an
grabs a pot, placing it under the faucet. She grabs another
pot and places it on the stove. She searches for a can opener
to open the peas. She moves back to the sink, shuts the
faucet and sees:

A waterbug crawling up the side of the pot from the drain.

                    ERIN
          Ugh! Goddamn it!

She bangs the pot onto the bug spilling the water and
upsetting Beth.

                    ERIN (cont'd)
          It's all right honey. Mommy's sorry. It's
          all right.

As she rocks Beth, who coughs in between tears, Erin looks
around - at her meager dinner and bug infested kitchen - and
is fed up with the whole day!

Camera follows her out the kitchen, into the main room where
she heads for a window, opens it and shouts to Matthew and
Kate in the sprinkler in the yard:

                    ERIN (cont'd)
          Matthew! Katie! We're going out.

INT. CHEAP DINER - TWILIGHT.

Beth is feeling better on Erin's lap. The two other kids sit
opposite in the booth. Erin is helping the kids read the menu
as the WAITRESS arrives.

                    MATTHEW
          Cheeseburger deluxe and a coke.

                    KATIE
                    (whispers across
                    table)
          Mommy can I get the cheeseburger deluxe
          with no cheese and no bread.

                          ERIN
                     (to Waitress)
               You get that?
                     (Waitress nods
                     and smiles)
               This one here'll have just a cup of that
               chicken broth and some crackers.

                          WAITRESS
               And for you?

                          ERIN
               Cup of coffee.

Waitress takes away menus and exits as Matthew asks:

                          MATTHEW
               You're not eating mom?

                          ERIN
               No, honey - my lawyer took me out to a big
               fancy lunch to celebrate and I'm still
               stuffed!

INT. ERIN'S HOUSE - NIGHT

The kids are asleep. A starved Erin is sitting at the kitchen
table, eating canned fruit cocktail.

O.C. Beth coughs. Coughs again. Erin looks up. Hopes it
doesn't turn into a coughing fit...

Beat.

INT. ERIN'S HOUSE - DAY

Erin sits down with the morning paper and turns to the
classifieds. She circles any jobs that look feasible.

LATER

Erin is on the phone, trying to reach Ed Masry. She leaves a
message.

EXT. PAY PHONE - DAY

Erin, holding Beth, tries again to reach Ed, with no success.

INT. ERIN'S HOUSE - DAY

Erin continues to look through the newspaper.

LATER

                                                     (CONTINUED)

CONTINUED:

Erin makes a call about a job. It's already been filled.

LATER STILL

Erin makes another call to Ed. Again she is told to leave a message. She hangs up, frustrated.

INT. MASRY & VITITOE - ED'S OFFICE - DAY

Midday. Ed enters with a cup of coffee in his hand. As he heads to his desk, he trips on a box of files. Coffee sloshes up out of his cut and on to his shirt.

> ED
> Damn it!
> (calling out)
> Brenda!!

She pops her head in.

> BRENDA
> Yeah?

He grabs a tissue, swabs his shirt, then kicks at the box.

> ED
> Who put that there?

> BRENDA
> It's those files you asked for.

> ERIN
> I didn't mean for you to leave them in the middle of the floor. Look at me. Get a towel, would you?

As Ed checks his reflection in the glass wall of his office, he notices, on the other side:

ERIN, standing in the middle of the secretaries' area, talking to DONALD, the office boy. Donald heads away from her.

> ED (cont'd)
> What's she doing here?

> BRENDA
> Who?

Ed goes to this office door and waves Donald over.

> ED
> Hey, Donald, what's she doing here?

CONTINUED:

                        DONALD
          She works here.

Ed looks back out at her -- what the hell?

INT. MASRY & VITITOE, MAIN ROOM - DAY

The support staff -- mostly middle-aged women -- are all
stealing glances at Erin. Ed approaches her, friendly.

                        ED
          Erin! How's it going?

Up close, the wear and tear of worry show on her face.

                        ERIN
          You never called me back. I left messages.

                        ED
          You did? Well, I, I didn't know that.
                    (beat)
          Listen, Donald seems to think that you
          said --

                        ERIN
          There's two things that aggravate me, Mr.
          Masry: Being ignored, and being lied to.

Glances skitter between the secretaries -- get a load of
this. Ed lowers his voice.

                        ED
          I never lied, Erin.

                        ERIN
          You said things would be fine and they're
          not. I trusted you.

                        ED
          I'm sorry about that. Really. But --

                        ERIN
          I don't need pity. I need a paycheck. And
          I've looked, but when you've spent the
          last six years raising babies, it's real
          hard to convince someone to give you a job
          that pays worth a damn.
                    (referring to
                    Brenda's
                    staring)
          You getting every word of this down,
          honey, or am I talking too fast for you!?

                                              (CONTINUED)

CONTINUED:

Brenda jumps. Ed sees everyone watching him, listening.

                    ED
          I'm sorry about that, I really am. But I
          have a full staff right now, so --

He starts to escort her out, but she stays put.

                    ERIN
          Bullshit. If you had a full staff, this
          office would return a client's damn phone
          calls.

She's backing him into a corner here. The secretaries
exchange knowing glances.

                    ERIN (cont'd)
          Now, I'm smart, I'm hard-working, and I'll
          do anything, and I'm not leaving here
          without a job.

C.U. on Erin as she steps in close to Ed and speaks in a low
voice that combines fierceness with desperation:

                    ERIN (cont'd)
          Don't make me beg. If it doesn't work out,
          fire me... But don't make me beg.

Ed looks at her for a long moment. Then:

                    ED
          No benefits.

INT. MASRY & VITITOE - FILE ROOM - DAY

A tight office neatly lined with file cabinets and shelves.
ANNA, the humorless file clerk, is showing Erin around.

                    ANNA
          ...what we do in here is file all of the
          cases. That way, at any time, we can tell
          the status of a file -- where it is in the
          office, stuff like that. We file 'em all
          here, alphabetically --

                    ERIN
          Simple enough.

                    ANNA
          And this is your desk.

                    ERIN
          Okay.

(CONTINUED)

CONTINUED:

                    ANNA
And now I want you to come with me. I want
to show you where the Xerox machine is.
Everybody has a code, and you need to know
about that.

                    ERIN
Do I get to pick my own code?

                    ANNA
We'll see.

INT. MASRY & VITITOE - ED'S OFFICE - DAY

Ed is packing up his office. Erin sticks her head in.

                    ERIN
Mr. Masry?

He turns, sees her.

                    ED
Yeah?

                    ERIN
I was wondering -- could you tell me who
I'd talk to about maybe getting an advance
on my paycheck? Just -- for the weekend.

                    ED
Rosalind's the officer manager. She
handles payroll and petty cash. But she
leaves early on Fridays.

                    ERIN
Oh. Okay. Thank you.

Ed looks at her a moment, sees that it's far from okay.

                    ED
Oh, for Pete's sake...

He takes out his wallet, looks in.

                    ED
All I have is hundreds.

                    ERIN
I don't wanna take your money, Mr. Masry.

                    ED
Where do you think your paycheck comes
from?

(CONTINUED)

CONTINUED:

He slaps a hundred in her hand and leaves. When he's gone
she looks at the bill -- her life raft.

EXT. BABY-SITTER'S HOUSE - NIGHT

Erin is at the door, taking Beth from the BABY-SITTER, a
shabby, unkept-looking woman in her 40's. Katie and Matt
pull on their backpacks and troop out of the sitter's house.

INT. ERIN'S HOUSE - MATT AND KATIE'S ROOM - NIGHT

A small room with Salvation Army furniture. A BUNCH OF
DAISIES is propped in a Ragu jar on Katie's bedside table.
Matt and Katie are asleep in bed. Erin looks down at them,
smiles, then kisses them good night.

INT. ERIN'S HOUSE - HALLWAY - NIGHT

Erin comes out of the bedroom and softly closes the door.
But just as the handle clicks into place, the house is filled
with the DEAFENING ROAR of a MOTORCYCLE, REVVING and REVVING.
It sounds as if it's gonna drive through the wall.

EXT. ERIN'S HOUSE - NIGHT

Erin steps out onto her front stoop and looks over at what
used to be Mrs. Morales' house. A few MOTORCYCLES are parked
on the lawn; A FEW BIKERS are drinking beer on the stoop; and
one asshole is one his bike, REVVING HIS ENGINE.

                    ERIN
          Hey!

But of course he can't hear her. She walks over to him,
stands right in his line of vision.

                    ERIN
          HEY!

He sees her and kills the engine. Everything about GEORGE
HALABY is tough-- his denim, his leather, his bike, his long
hair. Everything but his eyes, which twinkle like Santa's.

                    GEORGE
          Hello.

                    ERIN
          What are you doing making all that goddamn
          noise?

                    GEORGE
          Just introducing ourselves to the
          neighborhood.

                                        (CONTINUED)

CONTINUED:

                    ERIN
          Well, I'm the neighbors. There, now
          we're introduced, so you can shut the
          fuck up.

The guys on the porch chuckle. Erin turns and starts back to
her house. George hopes off his bike and follows her.

                    GEORGE
          Let's start over. My name's George. What's
          yours?

                    ERIN
          Just think of me as the person next door
          who likes it quiet.

                    GEORGE
          Now, don't be like that. Look, hell, we
          live next door to each other. And I feel
          bad.

Erin starts to go back in her house. George tails her.

                    GEORGE (cont'd)
          I feel terrible. I'm sorry. Will you
          accept my apology? I mean, hell, we're
          livin' right next door to each other. If
          you need a cup of sugar, or some cream.

                    ERIN
          I don't need sugar.

                    GEORGE
          You don't need any sugar. Well, why don't
          I take you out on a date to apologize for
          my rudeness?

Erin shakes her head in disbelief and keeps walking.

                    GEORGE (cont'd)
          You give me your number. I've already got
          your address, so you can't get away. I'll
          call you up proper and ask you out and
          everything.

She stops at her porch, turns to him.

                    ERIN
          You want my number?

                    GEORGE
          I do. I do want your number.

> ERIN
> Which number do you want, George?

> GEORGE
> You got more than one?

> ERIN
> Shit, yeah. I got numbers coming out of my
> ears. Like, for instance, ten.

> GEORGE
> Ten?

> ERIN
> Sure. That's how many months old my baby
> girl is.

> GEORGE
> You got a little girl?

> ERIN
> Yeah. Sexy, huh? How about this for a
> number? Six. That's how old my other
> daughter is. Eight is the age of my son.
> Two is how many times I've been married
> and divorced. Sixteen is the number of
> dollars in my bank account. 850-3943 is
> my phone number. And with all the numbers
> I gave you, I'm guessing zero is the
> number of times you're gonna call it.

She turns and heads inside. He calls out after her:

> GEORGE
> How the hell do you now your bank balance
> right off the top of your head like that?
> See that impresses me. And you're dead
> wrong about that zero thing, baby.

INT. MASRY & VITITOE - FILE ROOM - DAY

Erin is alone, filing as she talks on the phone.

> ERIN
> How long's she been crying like
> that?...Well, she's got that tooth coming
> in --

Ed appears in the door, carrying a box of files.

> ERIN (cont'd)
> Give her a cold washcloth to suck on --
> > (sees Ed)
> > (MORE)

CONTINUED:

                        ERIN (cont'd)
I gotta go -- there's a clean one in that
bag -- I'll check back in a bit.

She hangs up.

                        ED
Where's Anna?

                        ERIN
Out to lunch with the girls.

                        ED
Oh. Huh.
              (beat)
Well, look, I have to open a file. Real
estate thing. Pro-bono.

He plunks the box of papers & files on her desk. She stares
at it, with no idea of how to go about that.

                        ERIN
Oh. Okay.

He sees her staring at the box.

                        ED
You know how to do that, don't you?

                        ERIN
Yeah. I got it. No problem.

                        ED
Good.

Ed heads out, but pauses before leaving.

                        ED
You're a girl.

                        ERIN
Excuse me?

                        ED
How come you're not at lunch with the
girls? You're a girl.

                        ERIN
I guess I'm not the right kind.

Erin goes back to work. Ed starts out then stops.

                    ED
        Look, you may want to - I mean, now that
        you're working here - you may want to
        rethink your..wardrobe a little.

                    ERIN
        Why is that?

                    ED
        Well...I think maybe..some of the girls
        are a little uncomfortable because of
        what you wear.

                    ERIN
        Is that so? Well, it just so happens, I
        think I look nice. And as long as I have
        one ass instead of two, I'm gonna wear
        what I like if that's alright with you?

Ed hides a smile. He nods. As he exits, Erin returns to work
and remarks, without looking up....

                    ERIN (cont'd)
        You may want to re-think those ties..

Suddenly self-conscious, Ed looks down to his chest...

INT. MASRY & VITITOE - FILE ROOM - NIGHT

Erin is at her desk, staring bewildered at the files from the
box Ed gave her, which are now spread across her desktop.
She sees Anna packing up her things to leave.

                    ERIN
        Anna? With this real estate stuff --
        could you remind me, 'cause I'm a little
        confused about how exactly we do that.
        Why are there medical records and blood
        samples in real estate files?

                    ANNA
                (exasperated)
        Erin, you've been here long enough. If
        you don't know how to do your job by now,
        I am not about to do it for you.

EXT. BABY-SITTER'S HOUSE - EARLY EVENING.

Erin arrives to pick up her children from the unkept baby-
sitter. She knocks. No answer. She knocks and calls out.

CONTINUED:

No answer. She looks through window. It appears no one is there. She panics.

INT. ERIN'S HOUSE - EARLY EVENING.

Erin runs into her house calling her children's names. No answer. She is almost near tears with panic, rushing through each room. She grabs the phone to call the police when she hears-

The sound of her children laughing, outside.

                    ERIN
          Matthew! Katie!

EXT. ERIN'S HOUSE - EARLY EVENING.

She runs outside, trying to locate the voices. She follows the sounds of her children laughing and talking, towards the back of her yard, which sits across from:

EXT. GEORGE'S BACKYARD - EARLY EVENING

Katie and Matthew are sitting at a picnic table, eating hamburgers and hot dogs, barbecued by George, who sits opposite them with little Beth in his lap. They all seems right at home. Erin confused.

                    ERIN
          What the hell happened?

                    MATTHEW/KATIE
          Hi mom..

                    GEORGE
          Hey. You hungry?

                    ERIN
          What are they doing here? I went to pick
          them up-

                    GEORGE
          She came by about an hour ago. Said
          something came up and she had to drop the
          kids off.

                    ERIN
          Something came up! Why didn't she call me
          at work?

                    GEORGE
               (Erin is
               fearsome)
          I don't know. She..I..she..I don't know.

                                        (CONTINUED)

                                ERIN
                    THAT STUPID BITCH!

                              MATTHEW
                    MOM!

                                ERIN
                    Sorry!! I can't believe she just dumps my
                    kids off when nobody's home!!

                              GEORGE
                    I was home.
                              (Erin realizes
                              this)
                    They're fine. Seriously. We cooked some
                    hamburgers, had some milk.

                              MATTHEW
                    You want a hot dog? There's an extra one
                    on the grill.

The kids are being fed a full meal with clean plates and
napkins and glasses of milk. Beth acts like she's known
George all her life.

                              MATTHEW (cont'd)
                    What do you think about me getting a
                    tattoo?

Erin doesn't know what to say. George just smiles.

INT. ERIN'S HOUSE - LIVING ROOM - NIGHT

George is on the floor with Matt and Katie, playing war.
Katie points to the Harley emblem on his leather jacket. Both
kids are dressed for bed. Erin watches them interact with
George. She notices how good he is with them. How comfortable
they are with him.

                              KATIE
                    What's that stand for?

                              GEORGE
                    That's for Harley Davidson. The best damn
                    motorcycle ever made.

Erin comes in from the kitchen.

                                ERIN
                    And if I catch either of you anywhere near
                    one, I'll knock you silly. Brush your
                    teeth. And keep it down, the baby's
                    asleep.

CONTINUED:

They get up...

             GEORGE
        'Night.

             KATIE AND MATTHEW
        'Night.

...and head into bed. George starts cleaning up the cards.

             GEORGE
        Great kids.

Erin bends down to help him.

             ERIN
        Yeah, well..I'm sure I'll fuck them up
        eventually.

             GEORGE
        Why?

             ERIN
        I'm obviously not a good judge of
        character or I would have never left them
        with that idiot who cost a fortune and
        smelled like chicken fat. After I find her
        and kill her, I don't know what I'm going
        to do.

             GEORGE
        If you need help with them, I could do
        that.

             ERIN
        I'm not gonna leave my kids with you.

             GEORGE
        Why not?

             ERIN
        'Cause I don't even know you.

             GEORGE
        What do you want to know? Ask me.

             ERIN
        Look, thanks for today but-

             GEORGE
        You're welcome.

Erin doesn't know what to say.

                         GEORGE (cont'd)
What's the matter, you got so many friends
in this world, you can't use one more? I'm
serious. If you need someone to keep an
eye on them -- after school or something --
I don't have a job now, so I'm around in
the afternoons.

                         ERIN
Oh, that's a great recommendation. You're
unemployed?

                         GEORGE
By choice. I work when I need to.

                         ERIN
Yeah? And what do you do the rest of the
time, live off your trust fund?

                         GEORGE
I do construction, which pays real good.
And I make it last by living cheap.

                         ERIN
                    (with a little
                    laugh)
I hope that's not supposed to impress me.

                         GEORGE
Are you this hard on everyone who tries to
help you?

                         ERIN
I'm out of practice.

                         GEORGE
Then lemme remind you, the polite thing is
to say, thank you, it's a real nice offer,
I don't mind taking you up on it.

                         ERIN
Why in the hell would you want to watch my
kids?

                         GEORGE
'Cause I like kids. I like hanging out
with them.

                         ERIN
Right.

She starts cleaning up the cards.

CONTINUED: (3)

                        GEORGE
          I do. They keep it simple.

Erin thinks about the offer.

                        ERIN
          You're around every afternoon?

                        GEORGE
          Yup. Usually working on my bike.

She's tempted.

                        GEORGE (cont'd)
          No big deal. If it doesn't work out, you
          can send 'em back to the chicken fat lady.

Tempting. Erin looks him over, then, as she exits:

                        ERIN
          This isn't going to get you laid, you
          know.

George laughs.

                        GEORGE
          Well, that's good, because I didn't find
          you attractive either.

                        ERIN
          Well, good. Then we're even.

                        GEORGE
          So we don't have to worry about that. I'm
          so glad we got that out of the way.

                        ERIN
          Yeah, I feel much better.

                        GEORGE
          I do, too. Really, seriously, because now
          I can just look after the kids, and I
          don't have to worry about you coming onto
          me all the time.

Erin is amused.

INT. ERIN'S HOUSE - ERIN'S BEDROOM - NIGHT

The wee hours. Erin's in a T-shirt, holding Baby Beth in her
lap and sitting on her mattress on the floor. The paperwork
from the box is now spread all over the floor around her.
She's reading a letter.

                                              (CONTINUED)

CONTINUED:

CLOSE ON THE LETTER

it's from PG&E to Donna Peter Jensen. We see the phrases, "purchase your house...," "fair market value..."

CLOSE ON ANOTHER DOCUMENT

It's a list of comparable house sales in the area. Owner, cost; owner, cost. Every house is in the $65,000 range.

Erin lies down on the mattress and rests Beth on her chest. She set down the file she was reading and picks up another.

CLOSE ON THE FILE

It contains a letter from a Dr. Howard Reeves. The first paragraph contains the phrase "...medical examination of Donna and Peter Jensen..."

Toward the end of the letter there are two columns. One is headed: "IN RANGE". The other: "OUT OF RANGE". Under that heading appears the following: "lymphocytes, T-lymphocytes, natural killer cells, T Helpers, T8 suppressor cells"...

Erin stares at it, confused.

INT. ED'S OFFICE - DAY

Ed sits at his desk, on the phone.

                    ED
          ...well, describe it to me.

There's a knock. Erin enters, holding a file.

                    ED (cont'd)
          ...no, I mean, try it on and describe it
          to me. Yeah, bring the phone in with you.
          Sure they will. Mrs. Masry, don't be such
          a tease.
                    (sees Erin)
          Oh, babies, hold on, don't go away--

                    ERIN
          Hi. Sorry. Would you mind if I
          investigated this a little further?

                    ED
          Investigated what?

                    ERIN
          This real estate thing with the Jensens.
          The pro bono case...

CONTINUED:

                    ED
                (overlap)
        Oh yeah, yeah. yeah..

                    ERIN
                (overlap)
        See, yeah..I just want to make sure I'm
        understanding what I'm reading. So do you
        mind?

Distracted, Ed agrees without realizing what he's agreeing
to.

                    ED
        No, go ahead. Sure.

                    ERIN
        Great. Thanks.

Erin exits. Ed returns to his work.

EXT. L.A. FREEWAY - DAY

The beat-up old Hyundai heads east out of L.A.

EXT. HINKLEY, CA - DAY

This is a dry, desolate part of California. No downtown, no
community. Just tract after tract of arid farmland, with
small, bland, unprotected ranch homes cropping up out of
landscape like occasional tombstones.

A beat-up old sign on the road reads: "HINKLEY, CA. POP:"
but the corner where the number would be has broken off.

As a gust of wind lifts dust from the fields, Erin turns onto
Community Boulevard, the main road that cuts through Hinkley.
In doing so, she passes a nearby UTILITY PLANT. Its criss-
crossing PIPES and large COOLING TOWERS stand out clearly
against the flat, dry fields. Erin doesn't notice.

INT. ERIN'S HYUNDAI - DAY

Erin cruises through the neighborhood, looking at a piece of
paper with the Jensen's address on it. This area has seen
better days -- many of the houses have been razed, leaving
heaps of lumber and wire behind.

EXT. DONNA JENSEN'S HOUSE - DAY

A generic ranch home standing all alone in the middle of
nothing.

(CONTINUED)

CONTINUED:

There's a pool out back and a chain link fence hugging the
property. No landscaping. Dull, but clean. A few BOTTLES
OF SPRING WATER wait by the door.

The Hyundai pulls into the driveway and stops. Erin gets
out. As she heads up to the door, her spike heels sink into
the dirt. She rings the bell. It has a melody chime.

DONNA JENSEN opens the door. She's 35, petite, with a
scrappy, high-strung manner. She's wearing tight jeans, and
her dark curls are piled on top of her head.

                    ERIN
          Hi. Donna Jensen?

                    DONNA
          Yes?

                    ERIN
          I'm Erin Brockovich, from Masry and
          Vititoe?

                    DONNA
                (a little
                 surprised)
          You're a lawyer?

                    ERIN
          Hell, no. I hate lawyers. I just work
          for them. You got a minute?

INT. THE JENSENS' HOUSE - LIVING ROOM - DAY

The house is furnished with little money, but lots of care.
Erin's on a plaid couch, in a sea of needle point pillows.
Out back, two GIRLS, ages 9 and 11, are playing in a pool.

                    DONNA
          I don't mean to be a pain in PG&E's
          backside, especially after all they've
          done for Hinkley, but I look around here
          and I think, if they want this place,
          they're gonna have to pay for it.

                    ERIN
          So you didn't have the house up for sale -
          they just came to you and wanted to buy
          it?

                    DONNA
          Yeah. I don't want to move. Uproot the
          kids. I've got a couple of girls. Honest
          to God, I don't know if I have the energy.
          You know, I've been sick.
                (MORE)

                                          (CONTINUED)

CONTINUED:

> DONNA (cont'd)
> Me and Pete both have. So the whole idea
> of selling the house -- if they aren't
> gonna pay us properly, I just don't see
> the point.

> ERIN
> Yeah, I can see that.
> (beat)
> I guess the only thing that confused me is
> -- not that your medical problems aren't
> important, but -- how come the files about
> them are in with all the real estate
> stuff?

Donna tops off their iced teas.

> DONNA
> There's so much correspondence, I just
> keep it all in one place.

> ERIN
> Right, but -- I'm sorry, I don't see why
> you were corresponding with PG&E about it
> in the first place.

> DONNA
> Well, they paid for the doctor's visit.

> ERIN
> They did?

> DONNA
> You bet. Paid for a check-up for the
> whole family. And not like with insurance
> where you pay, then wait a year to be
> reimbursed, either. They just took care
> of it. Just like that. We never even saw
> a bill.

> ERIN
> Wow. Why would they do that?

> DONNA
> 'Cause of the chromium.

> ERIN
> The what?

> DONNA
> The chromium. Well, that's what kicked
> this whole thing off.

EXT. ERIN'S HYUNDAI - DAY

As Erin leaves Hinkley, she stops the car and takes a look at
the power plant she passed so obliviously on her way into
town.

Maybe it's the angle, or maybe it's what Donna's been telling
her, but somehow the plant seems more threatening now. Like
it's bearing down on the town.

EXT. UCLA CAMPUS - DAY

Erin walks past some students on her way to the Main Library.

INT. BUILDING CORRIDOR - DAY

Erin follows DR. FRANKEL down the hall.

                    FRANKEL
          What kind of chromium is it?

                    ERIN
          There's more than one kind?

                    FRANKEL
          Yes. There's straight-up chromium -- does
          all kinds of good things for the body.
          There's chrom 3, which is fairly benign,
          and then there's chrom 6 - hexavalent
          chromium, which, depending on the amounts,
          can be very harmful.

EXT. UCLA CAMPUS - DAY

Erin and Dr. Frankel continue walking.

                    ERIN
          Harmful, like -- how? What would you get?

                    FRANKEL
          With repeated exposure to toxic levels --
          God, anything, really -- from chronic
          headaches and nosebleeds to respiratory
          disease, liver failure, heart failure,
          reproductive failure, bone or organ
          deterioration -- plus of course, any type
          of cancer.

He rattles it off coolly. Just facts. Erin's stunned.

                    ERIN
          So that stuff -- it kills people.

                                        (CONTINUED)

CONTINUED:

                         FRANKEL
          Oh yeah. Definitely. Highly toxic,
          highly carcinogenic. Gets into your DNA,
          too, so you pass the trouble along to your
          kids. Very, very bad.

                         ERIN
          What's it used for?

                         FRANKEL
          A rust inhibitor. See, the utility plants
          run these piston engines to compress the
          gas, the engines get hot, you got to run
          water through them - chromium's in the
          water to prevent corrosion...

                         ERIN
          Well, how do I find-out what kind of
          chromium they use in Hinkley?

                         FRANKEL
          Have you been to their water board?

                         ERIN
          Hunh-uh. What's that?

                         FRANKEL
          Every county has one. They keep records
          of anything water-related within their
          jurisdiction. You should be able to find
          something there.

                         ERIN
          County Water Board. All righty, thanks.

                         FRANKEL
          Good luck.
                    (beat)
          Oh -- I wouldn't advertise what you're
          looking for if I were you... incriminating
          records have a way of disappearing when
          people smell trouble.

                         ERIN
          I'll remember that. Thanks.

EXT. LAHOTAN REGIONAL WATER BOARD - DAY

A small building on a small street baking under the desert
sun. Anybody with any sense is inside, out of the heat.

(CONTINUED)

CONTINUED:

Erin's Hyundai pull up and stops in a cloud of dust. Erin
hops out, checks her reflection in the side view mirror, then
heads into the building.

INT. LAHOTAN REGIONAL WATER BOARD - DAY

Drab, government-issue. SCOTT, the bored desk clerk is
thumbing his way through ROAD & TRACK. Just as he stops to
stare at a motor oil ad in which a buxom blond is straddling
the hood of a car, the huge door opens and Erin enters.

> ERIN
> Whew! God<u>damn</u>, that's a heavy door.

Scott looks up. It's like the girl from the ad walked right
off the page. He jumps up to help her with the door.

> SCOTT
> Oh, hey -- lemme give you a hand there.

> ERIN
> Thank you very much. Aren't you a
> gentleman? Mr....

> SCOTT
> Scott.

> ERIN
> Scott. Real pleased to meet you. I'm
> Erin.

She smiles. He can't believe his luck.

> SCOTT
> Erin. Cool. What can I do for you, Erin?

> ERIN
> Well, believe it or not, I am on the prowl
> for some water records.

> SCOTT
> (with a laugh)
> You come to the right place.

> ERIN
> (laughing along)
> I guess I did.

> SCOTT
> You just tell me what you want to look at
> and I'll be glad to dig 'em out for you.

CONTINUED:

>   ERIN
>   I wish I knew. It's for my boss. He's in
>   this water dispute, and he wants me to
>   find all manner of bills from all kinds of
>   places. The easiest thing would probably
>   be if I just squeezed·back there with you
>   and poked around myself. Would that be
>   okay?

>   SCOTT
>   Heck, yeah. Come on back. Just gonna
>   need you to sign in here --

He hands her a pen. He reads over her shoulder as she signs
her name -- Erin Pattee Brockovich.

>   SCOTT
>   Pattee? That your middle name?

>   ERIN
>   Nope. Maiden.

>   SCOTT
>   (disappointed)
>   You're married.

>   ERIN
>   Not anymore. Can I just..

She smiles and winks at him. He steps aside.

>   SCOTT
>   Yeah, just..

She goes around the counter with him and looks at the stacks
and stacks of files.

>   ERIN
>   I love your pants.

>   SCOTT
>   Thanks. This is it.

>   ERIN
>   It's impressive. Well, I'll call you if I
>   need anything.

She heads down an aisle, reading the spines of the files.
They're all town names-- Barstow, Victorville, Oro Grande,
Helendale -- in no particular order. Finally, Erin spots one
that says Hinkley. She pulls it down.

IN THE FILE

are pages and pages of Xeroxed memoranda, letters, charts, graphs, handwritten notes. All shoved in willy-nilly.

INT. WATER BOARD - NIGHT

Erin is on the floor, her legs stretched out in front of her. She has a bunch of files open and spread across the floor. The one in her hand has caught her attention.

INSERT ON THE PAPER

It's a memo titled: "CLEAN-UP AND ABATEMENT ORDER" from the water board to PG&E. Erin is concentrating hard on it, reading laboriously.

INT. MASRY & VITITOE - RECEPTION - DAY

CLOSE ON A XEROX OF THE ABATEMENT ORDER. WIDEN to see it is on top of a stack of papers that Erin is carrying as she enters the office. She has an efficient air about her -- a sense of purpose.

INT. MASRY & VITITOE - FILE ROOM - DAY

Erin swoops in, ready to work, only to find her desk cleared off. She turns to Anna, who's already hard at work.

                    ERIN
          Where's my stuff?

Anna looks up.

                    ANNA
          Where've you been?

                    ERIN
          What the fuck did you do with my stuff?

                    ANNA
          Don't use language with me --

But Erin's out the door before Anna can finish her sentence.

INT. MASRY & VITITOE - - DAY

Brenda is at her desk. Erin barrels in.

                    ERIN
          Someone stole my stuff.

                    BRENDA
          Nice to see you, Erin. We've missed you.

CONTINUED:

> ERIN
> I had photos of my kids, plus a mug --

Brenda reaches under her desk for a box, looks through it.

> BRENDA
> -- toothbrush, toothpaste, mousse and
> deodorant. Here.

> ERIN
> What's going on.

> BRENDA
> There may be jobs where you can disappear
> for days at a time, but this isn't one of
> them. Here, if you don't do the work, you
> don't get to stay.

She hands her the box. Erin doesn't take it.

> ERIN
> I've been working. Shit, that's all I've
> been doing. Ask Mr. Masry. He knows.

> BRENDA
> You ask Mr. Masry. He fired you.

INT. MASRY & VITITOE - ED'S OFFICE - DAY

Ed's at his desk, dialling the phone when Erin barrels in.

> ERIN
> You said to fire me?

He sets down the receiver.

> ED
> Erin, you've been gone for a week.

> ERIN
> I left a message. I've been dealing with
> that real estate thing. I was gonna write
> up a whole damn report and --

> ED
> That's not how we work here. You don't
> just leave a message and take off.

Brenda follows her in, still carrying the box of stuff.

> ERIN
> What am I supposed to do, check in every
> two seconds?

(CONTINUED)

CONTINUED:

                    BRENDA
          Yes. It's called accountability.

                    ERIN
          I'm not talking to you, bitch.

                    BRENDA
          Excuse me?

                    ERIN
                (yelling)
          Get out of my face!

                    ED
          Okay, enough.
                (beat)
          Now, look Erin -- this incident aside, I
          don't think this is the right place for
          you. So what I'm gonna do is make a few
          calls on your behalf. Find you something
          else, okay?

                    ERIN
          Don't bother.

She turns to Brenda, takes her box, and heads out.

                    ED
          Come on, I'm trying to help here.

                    ERIN
          Bullshit. You're trying to feel less
          guilty about firing someone with three
          kids to feed. Fuck if I'll help you do
          that.

Erin slams the file in Brenda's hand and leaves. Ed and
Brenda exchange a look.

                    ED
          Get back to work.

INT. ERIN'S HOUSE - MAIN ROOM - DAY

Erin enters, puts down the box and stares at the mail.
Bills, bills, and more bills. As she throws them on the
table, she sees George coming out of the kitchen.

                    ERIN
          What are you doing here?

                    GEORGE
          Fixing a leak under your sink.

                                        (CONTINUED)

CONTINUED:

She heads into the kitchen, weary and irritated.

                    ERIN
          I didn't ask you to do that. Damn it,
          George, I don't ask you to do things like
          that.

INT. ERIN'S HOUSE - KITCHEN- DAY

Erin enters, sees all the cleaning stuff from under the sink
is spread around the kitchen floor. A tool box lies open.

                    ERIN
          Look at this mess you've made.

                    GEORGE
          I'm not done with that yet. I'm gonna
          clean it up.

Erin gets down on her knees and starts putting things away.

                    GEORGE (cont'd)
          Relax, Erin, I'll do it -- I'm not --

Before he can finish, a huge WATER BUG runs onto Erin's hand.

                    ERIN
          Ugh -- <u>Jesus</u> --

She jumps and brushes it off. She takes her shoe and smacks
at the bug, missing it.

                    ERIN
          Where did it go?

The bug skitters away from her, along the floorboard. Erin
chases it, smacking at it repeatedly, missing it every time.

                    GEORGE
          It's right behind your foot.

But Erin keeps after it, corralling all her frustrations into
killing that one bug.

                    ERIN
          Get out of here!

                    GEORGE
          It's going up your leg now!

The bug crawls up onto the table, zipping behind the salt,
the paper, the napkin holder. Erin keeps after it, BANGING
the table harder and harder with each SMACK of her shoe.

(CONTINUED)

CONTINUED:

The salt and pepper skid off the table. The napkins fly from
their holder. Just as Erin's about to nail the bug, it slips
into a crack in the wall and disappears. Erin hurls her shoe
at the crack. It SMASHES into the wall.

As Erin stands there staring at the wall, her breath starts
to come heavily -- those deep breaths that precede tears. She
slowly slides down into a chair, defeat overcoming her.

                    ERIN (cont'd)
          Jesus! Who lives like this? Huh? Who
          lets her kids run around in a house
          crawling with bugs the size of housecats?

                    GEORGE
          It's a simple thing. Everybody gets them.
          All we gotta do is call an exterminator.

                    ERIN
          I <u>can't</u> call an exterminator. I can't
          afford one. God, I can't even afford my
          <u>phone</u>.
                    (beat)
          I got fired.

                    GEORGE
          It's a simple thing. Everybody gets them.
          All we gotta do is call an exterminator.

                    ERIN
          I <u>can't</u> call an exterminator. I can't
          afford one. God, I can't even afford my
          <u>phone</u>.
                    (beat)
          I got fired.

                    GEORGE
          What? But you've been working so hard --

                    ERIN
          Doesn't matter. Doesn't make one fucking
          bit of difference.

She exits. After a beat, George follows.

INT. ERIN'S HOUSE - ERIN'S BEDROOM - DAY

Erin sits on the bed, drying her eyes. George enters. Erin
looks up at herself in the mirror over her bureau.

                    ERIN
          I don't know what happened to me...

                                              (CONTINUED)

CONTINUED:

George listens by the door.

>   ERIN
>   I mean I was Miss Wichita, for Christ
>   sakes. Did I tell you that? Did ya know
>   you were living next door to a real live
>   fucking beauty queen?
>   (wipes her nose)
>   I still got the tiara. I thought it meant
>   I was gonna do something important with my
>   life, that I was gonna be someone.

>   GEORGE
>   You're someone to me.

He takes a step towards her and kneels in front of her, very
close. He takes her shoe from her hand and puts in back on
her foot. Then he takes her hands in his and kisses them.

>   ERIN
>   Are you going to be something else I have
>   to survive? Cause I'll tell you the truth,
>   I'm not up for it.

But he kisses her anyway. And for the first time in so long,
she feels like something other than a failure. He pulls her
into him, and she lets herself be pulled.

INT. ERIN'S HOUSE - ERIN'S BEDROOM - DAY

Erin re-enacts the Miss Wichita pageant for George.

>   ERIN
>   And I have this big bouquet of flowers,
>   and I have my foot out like this, and I
>   say...

As Erin recites her beauty queen speech, they are both
laughing at the naive, impossible goals of her youth;

>   ERIN
>   "....I will devote my entire reign as Miss
>   Wichita to bringing an end to world
>   hunger...and to the creation of a peaceful
>   earth for every man, woman and child..."

>   GEORGE
>   How long were you going to be Miss
>   Wichita?

>   ERIN
>   One year!
>   (George laughs)
>   (MORE)

CONTINUED:

                         ERIN (cont'd)
          Of course by the time I got through
          opening new supermarkets, I had just a few
          weeks left for hunger and world peace,
          so..Ha, ha, ha...damn..I don't know what
          the hell I was thinking.

He kisses one of her earlobes. Erin likes the sound of this
but it also makes her apprehensive.

                         ERIN (cont'd)
          What about you, huh?

                         GEORGE
          What about me?

                         ERIN
          What about you?

                         GEORGE
          Let me tell you something. You're a very
          special lady.

She leans in to kiss him, but before she does:

                         ERIN
          Don't be too nice to me, okay? It makes
          me nervous.

George looks almost hurt, but empathetic. Erin kisses him
long and hard as they begin to make love again.

INT. ERIN'S HOUSE - KITCHEN- DAY

CLOSE ON THE TABLE, where Beth is bobbling in her baby chair.
On one side of her is a heap of bills with "PAST DUE" and
"PLEASE REMIT" stamped on them. On the other, the well-
thumbed CLASSIFIED SECTION, with circles and X's all over it.

The DOORBELL rings. Erin swoops in and picks up Beth.

                         ERIN
          Come on, baby. Maybe that's Ed McMahon.

INT. ERIN'S HOUSE - FRONT DOOR - DAY

Erin carries Beth over to the front door, spies through the
peephole, and sees Ed standing there. She opens the door.

                         ERIN
          Wrong Ed.
                    (Ed looks
                    confused)
          What are you doing here?

                         ED
          I got an interesting call this afternoon.
          It was from a Doctor Frankel from UCLA.

                         ERIN
          Oh yeah?

                         ED
          He wanted you to know the legal limit for
          hexavalent chromium, is .05 parts per
          million. And that at the rate you
          mentioned, .58, it could be responsible
          for the cancers in that family you asked
          about. The Jensens.

                         ERIN
          Well, that was nice of him. Isn't it
          funny how some people go out of their way
          to help people and others just fire 'em.

                         ED
          Look, I'm sorry. You were gone. I just
          assumed you were off having fun.

                         ERIN
          Now, why in the hell would you assume
          that?

                         ED
          I don't know. Maybe 'cause you look like
          someone who has a lot of fun.

                         ERIN
          OH! So by that standard I should assume
          you never get laid.

Ed takes a beat, copping to the charge. He admits:

                         ED
          I'm married.
                    (Erin suppresses
                    a smile)
          So what's the story on this thing? This
          cancer stuff?

                         ERIN
          You wanna know, you gotta hire me back. I
          got a lot of bills to pay.

He glares at her. Realizes he has no choice.

                         ED
          Fine.

INT. ERIN'S HOUSE - LIVING ROOM - LATER

Erin has let Ed in. They're sitting.

                    ERIN
          ..so Donna had just put in these new
          cabinets - real nice, stained the wood and
          all - when she gets this call from
          somebody at PG&E saying that a freeway's
          gonna be built and they want to buy her
          house so they can make an off ramp for the
          plant...Meanwhile, the husband's sick with
          Hodgkins and she's in and out of the
          hospital with tumors - believe one thing
          has anything to with the other.

                    ED
          Because PG&E told her about the chromium.

                    ERIN
          Get this - they held a seminar. They
          invited about two hundred residents from
          the area. They had it at the plant in
          this warehouse.

Ed is listening with more and more interest.

                    ERIN (cont'd)
          ...Telling them all about Chromium 3 and
          how it was good for you, when all the time
          they were using Chromium 6.

Beat.

                    ED
          That document you found at the Water
          Board, the one that says it was the bad
          chromium -- you didn't happen to make a
          copy did you?

                    ERIN
          'Course I did.

                    ED
          Well, could I have a look at it?

Before getting it for him, she looks at him,

                    ERIN
          I want a raise. And benefits. Including
          dental.

CONTINUED:

                    ED
          Look, Erin, this is not the way I do
          business.

                    ERIN
          What way is that?

                    ED
          Extortion.

Erin doesn't budge.

                    ED
          Okay. A five percent raise, and we'll
          talk about benefits later.

                    ERIN
          Ten.
               (off his look)
          There's a lot other places I could work.

                    ED
          A ten percent raise and benefits. But
          that's it. I'm drawing the line.

                    ERIN
               (mock whisper, to Beth)
          He's drawing the line.

She goes to her box of stuff from the office and digs out the
document for him. He scans it.

                    ED
          This is the only thing you found?

                    ERIN
          So far. But that place is a pig sty. I
          wouldn't be surprised if there's more.

                    ED
          I know how those places are run. They're
          a mess. What makes you think you can just
          walk in there and find what we need?

                    ERIN
          They're called boobs, Ed.

Shaking his head, Ed rises to leave.

EXT. 10 FREEWAY - DAY

Erin's Hyundai zips along the freeway.

(CONTINUED)

CONTINUED:

Erin's driving. Matthew's in the front seat. Katie and Beth
(in a car seat) are in the back.

EXT. WATER BOARD - DAY

The sound of a BABY CRYING. The Hyundai's parked in front.

INT. WATER BOARD - DAY

Erin is at the Xerox machine, copying a file while she tries
to calm Beth. There's a stack of files on the nearby table.
Matthew and Katie are flopping around on the floor.

Scott is on the phone with someone - we don't know who - but
the look on his face is one of anxiety. His eyes keep
shifting between the call and Erin. He nods as if he
understands and hangs up... He crosses to her.

                    SCOTT
                (real friendly)
          So, how we doin?

                    ERIN
          We're doing great.

                    SCOTT
                (off the cuff)
          Good..Well, you've got quite a lot done
          already..so uhh...I'm sorry but uh...we
          ...we have to have those records back now.

Erin stops..looks at him..and quickly knows how to respond;

                    ERIN
          No.

                    SCOTT
          What?

                    ERIN
          These papers are a matter of public
          record. I'm not leaving til they're
          copied.

Erin returns to copying. Scott is stymied.

INT. MASRY & VITITOE - BRENDA'S DESK - DAY

Ed comes in in the morning, and without pausing, hands Brenda
a copy of the STACK OF DOCUMENTS, with a Post-It on the top.

                    ED
          Fax these to this number, okay?

                                              (CONTINUED)

CONTINUED:

                          BRENDA
         All of 'em?

                          ED
         All of them.

He continues into his office and closes the door.

CLOSE ON THE FAX MACHINE LED

Brenda types in the number. The recipient's ID comes up on
the LED: PG&E CLAIMS DEPT.

INT. JENSEN HOUSE - LIVING ROOM - DAY

Donna has made lunch for Erin. The remnants are on the
coffee table. A copy of those DOCUMENTS are in Donna's
hands. She's on her couch reading them. Outside, Donna's
two daughters are playing in the pool. She reads the last
page and looks up at Erin, bewildered.

                        DONNA
         An on-site monitoring well? That means --

                        ERIN
         It was right up on that PG&E property over
         there.

                        DONNA
         And you say this stuff, this hexavalent
         chromium -- it's poisonous?

                        ERIN
          Yeah.

                        DONNA
         Well -- then it's gonna be different than
         what's in our water, 'cause ours is okay.
         The guys from PG&E told me. They sat
         right there in the kitchen and said it was
         fine.

                        ERIN
         I know. But the toxicologist I've been
         talking to? He gave me a list of problems
         that can come from hexavalent chromium
         exposure. And everything you all have is
         on that list.

Donna resists this idea hard.

CONTINUED:

                    DONNA
        No. Hunh-uh, see that's not what the
        doctor said. He said one's got absolutely
        nothing to do with the other.

                    ERIN
        Right, but PG&E paid for that doctor.

Donna sits quietly, trying to make sense of this. The only
sound is the LAUGHING and SPLASHING from the pool out back.
Then, gradually, Donna realizes what it is she's hearing --
her kids playing in toxic water. She jumps up...

                    DONNA
        ASHLEY! SHANNA!

...and runs out to the pool.

EXT. DONNA'S HOUSE - DAY

Erin watches Donna run to the edge of the pool in a frantic
response to this news.

                    DONNA
        OUT OF THE POOL! BOTH OF YOU, OUT OF THE
        POOL, <u>RIGHT NOW</u>!

                    SHANNA
        How come?

                    DONNA
        'CAUSE I SAID SO, THAT'S WHY, NOW GET OUT!
        OUT! NOW!!!

Erin watches compassionately as Donna flails to get her kids
out of the contaminated water.

INT. ED'S OFFICE - DAY

Ed is attempting to tie his tie in a mirror, as Erin looks
on. He's very excited as he fumbles the knot...

                    ED
        I'm telling you, the minute Brenda sent
        the fax -- I'm talking the second she
        pressed that send button -- PG&E claims
        department is on the phone to me,
        scheduling a meeting.

                    ERIN
        So you think we...let me do this, you're
        driving me nuts...

CONTINUED:

She makes him face her as she ties his tie....

> ERIN
> You think we scared 'em, don't you?

> ED
> Well, they're taking the trouble to send
> someone. It sure as hell sounds like
> they're sitting up and taking notice. Now
> do me a favor, and let me handle this.

INT. MASRY & VITITOE, MAIN ROOM - DAY

Ed and Erin come out and see DAVID FOIL waiting at reception.
Forget law school, this kid looks like he's just out of
twelfth grade. Not a hair on his chin. His suit and shoes
look brand new.

Ed stops suddenly, before being seen. Erin stops too.

Ed's expression upon seeing the "young" representative tells
us he's none too happy.

INT. MASRY & VITITOE - CONFERENCE ROOM - DAY

Ed and Erin are seated across the table from Foil. To say
this kid lacks authority is a gross understatement. He
doesn't talk; he squeaks.

> FOIL
> ...in the interest of putting this whole
> thing to rest, PG&E is willing to offer
> the Jensens 250,000 dollars for their
> home.

Ed laughs a little in disbelief.

> ED
> 250,000?

> FOIL
> In terms of land value out in Hinkley, Mr.
> Masry, we feel it's more than fair price.

> ED
> What about it terms of medical expenses?
> 250,000 doesn't come close to what this
> family's gonna have to spend on doctors.

> FOIL
> I understand they've had a bad run of
> luck, health-wise, and they have my
> sympathies. But that's not PG&E's fault.

(CONTINUED)

CONTINUED:

                        ED
          You're kidding, right?

Foil doesn't answer.

                        ED (cont'd)
          Look at these readings. PG&E's own
          technicians documented toxic levels of
          hexavalent chromium in those test wells on
          numerous occasions.

Ed shoves them across the table. Foil doesn't look at them.

                        ED (cont'd)
          Everything the Jensens have had is proven
          reaction to exposure to hexavalent
          chromium. They've had...

He stalls a moment. Erin jumps in.

                        ERIN
          -- breast cysts, uterine cancer, Hodgkin's
          disease, immune deficiencies, asthma,
          chronic nosebleeds.

Despite their persuasiveness, Foil parrots what is obviously
the party line:

                        FOIL
          A million things could have caused those
          problems. Poor diet, bad genes,
          irresponsible lifestyle. Our offer is
          final and more than fair.

                        ED
          Wait a minute -- I thought we were
          negotiating here.

                        FOIL
          250,000 is all I'm authorized to offer.

Ed looks across at this pissant little kid. Then stands.

                        ED
          I will present your offer to my clients.
          I doubt they'll accept it.

As Ed starts out, Foil tries to take a stand;

CONTINUED: (2)

                             FOIL
Mr. Masry, before you go off on some
crusade, you might want to remember who it
is you're dealing with here. PG&E is a
twenty-eight-billion dollar corporation.

                             ED
                     (smiles, acting
                       excited/greedy)
Twenty-eight billion dollars! I didn't
know it was THAT much! WOW!

Foil suddenly realizes he's made a mistake admitting the
company's wealth. Ed leaves the conference room. Erin
follows him out.

INT. MASRY & VITITOE, MAIN ROOM - DAY

Erin follows Ed as he stomps back to his office.

                            ERIN
At least they made an offer.

                             ED
                     (undoing his
                     tie)
That wasn't an offer. A million would
have been an offer. When they send the
god damn mail clerk down to jerk me off,
waste me time.

Ed throws the tie off.

                            ERIN
Why would they do that?

                             ED
Because they can. You heard that kid --
they have twenty-eight billion dollars at
their disposal. They can afford to waste
all the time in the world!

                            ERIN
And you can't?

                             ED
What, you think I'm made of money?!

                            ERIN
What are you yelling at me for?

                            ED
Because I'm pissed off!

                                    (CONTINUED)

CONTINUED:

> > > ERIN
> > > (yells back)
>
> Good!

> > > ED
>
> FUCK YOU!

> > > ERIN
>
> FUCK YOU BACK!

Erin starts to smile. Ed cracks a smile then starts to laugh.

> > > ED
>
> I really hate you sometimes, ya know that.

> > > ERIN
>
> No, you love me.

INT. MASRY & VITITOE - OUTSIDE ED'S OFFICE - NIGHT

End of the day. Most everyone has left. Erin is at her new work space near Ed's office. She's pouring over a fat file of documents. Rosalind wanders by with her coat on.

> > > ROSALIND
>
> You've been reading for hours.

> > > ERIN
>
> I'm a slow reader.

Whatever she thinks of her, Rosalind can't help but see Erin's hard at work. She turns on Erin's desk lamp and heads out - it's the first helpful hand Erin has received from one of the women.

Erin turns back to her work when her attention is then drawn to the big glass office doors; on the other side, Rosalind is talking to a lost-looking COUPLE IN THEIR MID-30'S. These are MANDY and TOM ROBINSON. He's in a security guard uniform, with an envelope under his arm. Rosalind points to Erin. The Browns enter the office and approach her.

> > > MANDY
>
> Excuse me, are you Erin Brockovich?

> > > ERIN
>
> Yeah. Who are you?

> > > TOM
>
> I'm Tom Robinson. This is my wife Mandy.
> We used to live across the street from the
> Jensens. I think you know Donna.

CONTINUED:

                         ERIN
                Yeah.

                         TOM
                PG&E bought our house last year.

INT. ERIN'S DESK - LATER

CLOSE ON PHOTOS OF CHICKENS, each with twisted, limp legs.

                         TOM
                Vet said they were filled with tumors and
                stuff. They couldn't walk.

WIDEN to see Erin looking at them with Tom and Mandy.

                         ERIN
                Wow. How many were born like this?

                         TOM
                Twelve, maybe thirteen.

                         MANDY
                When Donna told us about you, and what you
                told her about the chromium, we figured
                that might have something to do with this,
                too.

                         ERIN
                Yeah, it might. May I keep these?

She tucks them into a file, as if that's it.

                         ERIN (cont'd)
                Thank you so much. I really appreciate
                it.

                         MANDY
                There's something else, too.

                         ERIN
                What?

                         TOM
                Well. Mandy here's had five miscarriages.

                         ERIN
                I'm so sorry.

                         MANDY
                I figured it musta been something I did,
                like when I smoked marijuana, maybe. Or
                took birth control pills.
                         (MORE)

CONTINUED:

                    MANDY (cont'd)
But then Donna told me you thought this
chromium might be to blame for her
problems, so I figured...

INT. ERIN'S HOUSE - NIGHT

Erin enters, exhausted. She collapses on a chair.

George is on his hands and knees apparently searching for a
lost toy. Erin talks to him with her eyes closed.

                    ERIN
I got to take a bath.

                    GEORGE
You should go in.

                    ERIN
They're not asleep?

                    GEORGE
Katie and Beth are.

They exchange a look. Erin knows Matthew's upset.

INT. ERIN'S HOUSE - MATTHEW AND KATIE'S ROOM - NIGHT

Matthew and Katie are in bed, with the lights off. Erin
comes in, quietly, in clothes from work.

                    ERIN
Hey.

CLOSE ON MATTHEW. He's awake and pissed. She sits on his
bed. She knows he's mad at her - she speaks softly,
caringly;

                    ERIN
How was school?

                    MATTHEW
Fine.

                    ERIN
Did you do your homework?

                    MATTHEW
Yeah.

                    ERIN
Any problems?

He doesn't answer. She comes in and pulls up the covers.

CONTINUED:

                    ERIN
          I know you're upset. But the way this job
          is, things come up at the last minute,
          real important things that I gotta deal
          with.

                    MATTHEW
                    (cutting her off)
          Fine!

                    ERIN
          Please don't be mad at me. I'm..I'm doing
          this for us...I know it's hard for you to
          understand but..I mean, don't you want
          mommy to be good at her job?
                    (no answer)
          And it's not like I miss dinner all the
          time. We all ate together last night.

                    MATTHEW
                    (from under the
                    covers)
          You were reading the whole time.

He's got a point there. Erin feels like shit.

                    ERIN
          Okay.

EXT. ROUTE 10, INLAND EMPIRE - DAY

Ed's big old Mercedes is tooling down the freeway at a rate
well below the speed limit.

EXT. JENSEN'S HOUSE - NIGHT

The Mercedes and a truck are parked out front.

                    PETE (O.S)
          There's something about this whole thing I
          don't quite understand, Mr. Masry.

INT. DONNA JENSEN'S HOUSE - LIVING ROOM - NIGHT

Donna and Pete Jensen, and Mandy and Tom Robinson are all
seated, sipping iced tea. While they talk, Erin hands them
all information packets on chromium. Ed is standing in front
of them, a little stiff.

                    PETE
          If PG&E messed with our water, why would
          they bother saying anything about it to
          us? Why not just keep quiet about it?

                    ED
          To establish a statute of limitations
          See, in a case like this, you only have a
          year from the time you first learn about
          the problem to file suit. So PG&E
          figures, we'll let the cat out of the bag -
          - tell the people the water's not perfect;
          if we can ride out the year with no one
          suing, we'll be in the clear forever.

                    DONNA
          But it was more than a year ago that they
          told us --

                    ED
          It's okay. We're not suing.

                    ERIN
          Not yet.

                    ED
                 (annoyed at that
                 remark)
          All we're doing is using this information
          to get you a real nice purchase price on
          your house, and get you two --
                 (to the Robinsons)
          -- a comparable retroactive bonus added to
          your sale price. This way PG&E can still
          look good to their shareholders, 'cause
          they're not involved in a ugly lawsuit;
          all they're doin is buying a little
          property.

Tom looks up from his retainer agreement.

                    TOM
          It doesn't say here how much this whole
          thing's gonna cost us.

                    ED
          My fee's forty percent of whatever you get
          awarded.

Erin watches them look around at each other, stunned by the
figure.

                    ERIN
          Boy, do I know how you feel. First time I
          heard that number, I said you got to be
          kidding me. Forty goddamn percent?

                          ED
          Erin --

                          ERIN
          I'm the one who's injured, and this joker
          who sits at a desk all day is gonna walk
          away with almost half my reward?

                          ED
          Erin --

Erin's enjoying Ed's discomfort almost too much to stop. But
just almost. She shifts gears.

                          ERIN
          Then I asked him how much he makes if I
          didn't get anything.

They look at Ed. Well?

                          ED
          Then I don't get anything either.

                          ERIN
          Plus he's out all of the costs. So I
          realized, he's taking a chance too.

When they hear this, and realize he's in it with them, they
all reach for their pens and sign. They hand the agreements
over to Erin, who takes them across the room to Ed. He
stuffs them in his briefcase and closes it up. That's that.

                          ED
          All right, then.

                          DONNA
          I made a bundt cake. I'll put on some
          coffee. Who wants coffee and cake?

                          ERIN
          I do.

                          ED
          Thank you, but we have to be getting back.

Boy. Cold as ice. Erin stares at him, stunned by his
brusque manner, then leans into him, close.

                          ERIN
                    (whispering)
          Have a fucking cup of coffee, Ed.

She gives him a stern look. Ed turns to Donna.

                         ED
          Coffee would be great, thank you.

                         ERIN
          I'll help you.

She picks up a tray of iced tea and cookies and heads to the
kitchen. Donna and Mandy follow, leaving Ed alone with Pete
and Tom. He stands there, awkwardly.

                         PETE
          My wife makes really good bundt cake.

                         ED
          I love bundt cake.

EXT. LINWOOD DAIRY - BARN - DAY

Another day. BOB LINWOOD, 40's and gruff, is in the barn,
tossing hay around.

                         LINWOOD
          ...Seems like someone in the family ended
          up with a rash somehow. And, seemed like,
          no matter what we did for it...always come
          back.

                         ERIN
          Over what period of time?

                         LINWOOD
          Long time. You know, years. I never did
          keep track of it. Kids are sick. Animals
          need to be fed. Just couldn't get rid of
          it, that's all.

INT. LAURA AND MIKE AMBROSINO'S HOUSE - NIGHT

Erin is talking to MIKE and LAURA AMBROSINO -- 30's. Solid,
family folks. But Laura's left brow and cheekbone look
swollen and misshapen, and she's trying to hide the fact that
she's in a lot of pain.

                         ERIN
          Mrs. DeSoto said she wasn't sure exactly
          what it was that you had --

                         LAURA AMBROSINO
          Oh, well, we know what it is.

                         MIKE AMBROSINO
          They know - it's gastrointestinal..

                                              (CONTINUED)

CONTINUED:

                    LAURA AMBROSINO
                       (overlapping)
          Gastrointestinal cancer.

                    MIKE AMBROSINO
          Yeah. She got sick about n..nine months
          ago.

                    LAURA AMBROSINO
          Nine months ago.

                    MIKE AMBROSINO
          And they operated on her about six months
          ago.

                    LAURA AMBROSINO
          The intestine.

                    ERIN
          Right.

EXT. PAMELA DUNCAN'S HOUSE - DAY

Erin stands at the front door and rings the bell. After a
moment;

PAMELA DUNCAN opens the door, a cup of coffee in her hand.
By her distant, cautious attitude, we immediately sense a
difference between her and the other Hinkley residents.

                    ERIN
          Hi. My name is Erin Brocko—

                    PAMELA
          I know who you are. Donna called me.

                    ERIN
          Oh... May I come in?

                    PAMELA
          I told Donna we're not interested in
          getting involved.

Beat.

                    ERIN
          Can I ask you why?

                    PAMELA
          What's the point?

                                              (CONTINUED)

CONTINUED:

                    ERIN
          Donna told me you've been sick. Your kids
          were sick...

Pamela gets angry at the mention of her kids.

                    PAMELA
          You people don't give a shit. Anything to
          get what you want!

Slams the door in her face.

INT. RITA AND TED DANIEL'S HOUSE - DAY

Erin is talking to TED and RITA DANIELS. Their daughter
ANNABELLE, 10, is sitting on the couch, wrapped in a blanket.

                    ERIN
          Well, it's just so good of you to have me
          in when I just stopped by like that.

                    TED
          Oh, well, it's a good day to come by.
          She's feeling pretty good today.

                    RITA
          She's doing well today.

                    ERIN
          Mike Ambrosino remembered seeing you folks
          at the hospital from time to time. So
          that's what brought me out here.

                    TOM
          Yeah, we've been there from time to time.

                    ERIN
                (to Annabelle)
          And you. Whew, are you ever a beauty. I
          mean, you must drive those boys crazy. I
          can see it in your eyes. You drive them
          wild.

Annabelle smiles a little. Erin smiles back, almost fixated
on her.

                    ERIN (cont'd)
          You do, don't you? Torture 'em. It's good
          for them.

                    TOM
          Uh, don't teach her anything too early.

(CONTINUED)

CONTINUED:

                    RITA
          Yeah, she can't wait to get on her new
          dress. Isn't that right?

                    TED
          She wants to go back to school. We're
          trying to hopefully do that in the next
          couple of months.

                    RITA
          Yeah, get her out of her nightgown here.

                    TED
          She's gonna do it.

                    RITA
          Yeah.

EXT. VALLEY SIDEWALK - DAY

Ed and Erin are walking down the street, take-out coffee cups
in their hands. Ed is sipping his, but Erin is in too much
of a lather to drink hers.

                    ED
          Hunh-uh. Absolutely not.

                    ERIN
          That's crazy-- why not?

                    ED
          The only reason PG&E's even talking to us
          is 'cause this is a quiet little real
          estate dispute. We add plaintiffs, and
          suddenly we're in the middle of a toxic
          tort -- with a statute problem -- against
          a massive utility. No, thank you.

They go into their office building.

EXT. OFFICE COURTYARD - DAY

Erin and Ed walk toward the office.

                    ERIN
          Okay, so here's what I'll do. I'll go on
          up to Ted and Rita Daniels -- two of the
          nicest people you'd ever hope to meet, who
          spend every single day watching their
          little girl fight like a dog against this
          cancer -- I'll tell them we can't help
          them 'cause you don't wanna work hard.

CONTINUED:

                    ED
                (turns on her)
        Work hard!!? Why you little...Let me tell
        you something - I've worked all my life. I
        built a firm and kept it alive through
        lawsuits, injunctions, and evictions. I
        have survived a quadruple bypass, cancer,
        being born with one kidney and having
        diabetes...

Erin's genuinely impressed as Ed continues;

                    ED (cont'd)
        ...I have personally managed to save a
        million dollars over more than thirty
        years of getting some clients ten times
        that. Don't tell me I don't work hard!
        Don't tell me I don't have the right to
        stop...to take a breath and enjoy my life.

Erin is smart enough to know when to listen. So she does. And
she waits...

                    ED (cont'd)
        -- And what the hell do you know about any
        of this anyway!? Something like this, Erin
        -- it could take forever. They're a huge
        corporation. They could bury us in
        paperwork for the next fifteen years. I'm
        just a guy with a private firm.

She makes her move-

                    ERIN
        -- who happens to know they poisoned
        people and lied about it.

The doors open. Ed gets off. Erin follows.

INT. MASRY & VITITOE - DAY

Erin tails Ed back to his office.

                    ERIN
        We can get these people. With a little
        effort, I really think we can nail their
        asses to the wall.

                    ED
        Oh you do? With all your legal expertise,
        you believe that?

CONTINUED:

                     ERIN
           Don't you ever just know?

Erin speaks with such calm sincerity, it stops Ed for a
moment. She thinks she's getting to him.

                     ED
           Do you also "just know" where the money's
           going to come from? That's why most of
           these cases settle--lack of money. Do you
           know what toxicologists and geology
           experts costs? We'd be looking at a
           hundred grand a month, easy. I've already
           made a huge dent in my savings.

                     ERIN
           We'll figure it out. Look,, I admit I don't
           know shit about shit. But I know the
           difference --

He moves away and shuts his office door on her.

                  ERIN (CONT'D)
           -- BETWEEN RIGHT AND WRONG!

The office is staring.

                    BRENDA
           Lovers' quarrel?

                     ERIN
           Oh, bite my ass, Krispy Kreme!
               (to the others)
           I feel you looking at me!

INT. ED'S OFFICE - DAY

Ed goes over to his desk, sits down. He sees a stack of
messages there, starts flipping through them. Then he stops.

INT. MASRY & VITITOE - DAY

Ed opens the door, surprised to find her still there.

                     ERIN
           I'm sorry.

                     ED
           How many families we talking about here?

                     ERIN
           Four more. Eleven people. So far.

                         ED
          You think there's more?

                         ERIN
          Well -- I found one document at the water
          board that had a toxic test well reading
          from 1967. A hell of a lot of people have
          lived on that land since then.

Ed pauses, groans again, realizing what decision he's making.

                         ED
          This is a much different ball game, Erin.
          A much bigger deal.

                         ERIN
          Kind of like David and what's-his-name?

                         ED
          Kind of like David and what's-his-name's
          whole fucking family.
                    (heavy sigh)
          Okay, here's the deal -- if, and only if,
          you find me the evidence to back all this
          up -- I'll do it. I'll take it on.

She smiles victoriously.

                         ERIN
          You're doing the right thing, Mr. Masry.

                         ED
          Yeah, yeah. Remind me of that when I'm
          filing for bankruptcy.

                         ERIN
          'Course, gathering evidence -- now, that's
          a big job. A hell of a lot bigger than
          just filing. I'm gonna be working a lot
          harder now, taking on a lot more
          responsibility...

He gives her a look. Knows what's coming.

                         ED
                    (overlaps, to himself)
          I don't believe this-

                         ERIN
                    (overlapping)
          Another raise wouldn't hurt.
                    (MORE)

CONTINUED: (2)

>   ERIN (cont'd)
> And with all the time I'm gonna be
> spending in my car, I'll probably be
> needing my own cell phone, won't I?

>   ED
> I don't believe this.

>   ERIN
> Just a little phone?

Ed closes the door on her. Erin smiles as she crosses back
to her desk.

EXT. HINKLEY - ROADSIDE DITCH - DAY

Erin is straddling a ditch, scooping clumps of gunky moss
from the ditch into plastic containers. Over this:

As Erin labels the containers, she slides down the side of
the ditch, and lands smack in it, knee-deep in gunk.

EXT. HINKLEY - COMMUNITY BOULEVARD - NIGHT

Erin, now completely dirty, is climbing over a fence marked
"No Trespassing". Her arms are full of more containers.

She adds them to a growing collection of containers in the
trunk of her car.

EXT. HINKLEY - THE POOL BEHIND AN ABANDONED HOUSE - DAY

Another day. Erin minces her way down to the deep end of the
pool.

She gets to the deep end and scoops up a Ziploc full of
rancid pool water and seals it.

Erin spots a few dead frogs in the water. She picks one up
by the leg, and seals it in a plastic bag as well.

EXT. WELL - DAY

With a sample cup held in her teeth, Erin hauls herself up
over the well's concrete wall, then, with her back against
one side of the well and her feet against the other, starts
shimmying down the well.

INSIDE THE WELL

She winces at the algae and gook that's clinging to her as
she descends to the water level. When she's low enough, she
takes the sample cup from her teeth and scoops up the water.

EXT. WELL - DAY

Erin raises herself up to see:

TWO GUARDS heading straight for her.

She campers to her feet and runs. The Guards pursue - chasing her off the property....

INT. ERIN'S HOUSE - NIGHT

It's a hot night. George is playing on the floor with the kids. Erin is behind them on the couch, laboriously reading a book labeled, simply, CHROMIUM. The phone RINGS. Erin picks it up.

                    ERIN
          Hello?

                    MALE VOICE (O.S)
          Is this the Erin Pattee Brockovich that's
          been snooping around the Water Board?

His voice is flat, creepy. Not friendly

                    ERIN
          Yes. Who's this?

                    MALE VOICE
          You should watch your step. A young lady
          like yourself with three young children..

                    ERIN
                    (overlapping)
          Who is this?

                    MALE VOICE
          Do you understand what I'm saying?

CLICK. Erin stares at the phone, freaked.

INT. ERIN'S HOUSE - FRONT DOOR - NIGHT

George watches Erin double-checking the locks on the door.

                    ERIN
          I'm not gonna quit 'cause of one creepy
          phone call, George.

                    GEORGE
          Come on, Erin. A job's supposed to pay
          your bills, not put you in danger.

(CONTINUED)

CONTINUED:

                        ERIN
          I'm not in danger. I mean, the phones
          might be tapped -

                        GEORGE
                     (overlaps)
          What?

                        ERIN
                     (overlaps)
          But that's usual. And we have a dead bolt.
          It's not a big deal.

She goes to the living room, double-checks the window locks
in there. George follows.

                        GEORGE
          Look, don't you think you might be out of
          your league here?

                        ERIN
          No, see -- that's exactly what those
          arrogant PG&E fucks want me to think --
          But you know what? They're wrong.

She heads in the bedrooms.

                        GEORGE
          It doesn't have to be this complicated,
          Erin. There's a lot of jobs out there.

                        ERIN
                     (offhand)
          How would you know?

George reacts, a little stung. He follows her into:

INT. MATT AND KATIE'S BEDROOM - NIGHT

Matt and Katie are asleep. Erin is checking their windows.
George comes in. They whisper.

                        GEORGE
          You mind telling me what that's supposed
          to mean?

                        ERIN
          Nothing. I'm sorry.

                        GEORGE
          If you got a problem with me taking care
          of your kids instead of getting some job,
          just say so.

                              ERIN
                    I didn't say that.

                              GEORGE
                    'Cause I can get a job. I will. And you
                    can start leaving the kids with the
                    chicken fat lady again.

                              ERIN
                    Oh, come on. Jesus, I said I'm sorry.
                    Keep your voice down.

                              GEORGE
                    I know what they can sleep through, Erin.
                    I probably know it better than you.

She gives him a glare, then leaves the room.

INT. WATER BOARD - DAY

Erin is reaching up to a high shelf for a dusty old box of
files. Out of the corner of her eye, she sees Scott passing.

                              ERIN
                    Hey, Scott. Tell me something. Does PG&E
                    pay you to cover their ass, or do you just
                    do it out of the kindness of your heart?

                              SCOTT
                    I don't know what you're talking about.

                              ERIN
                    The fuck you don't. No one calls me
                    Pattee. That heavy-breathing sicko that
                    called the other night could've only found
                    out about me from you.
                              (beat)
                    People are dying, Scott. You've got
                    document after document here, right under
                    your nose, that says why, and you haven't
                    said word one about it. I wanna know how
                    the hell you sleep at night.

Scott is speechless. He just stands there. Erin drags the
box to the floor and goes to work.

INT. ERIN'S HYUNDAI - NIGHT

A pile of documents is strapped into the passenger seat. An
empty coffee cup rolls around the floor. Erin's driving,
exhausted. She yawns as she dials her phone.

                                                        (CONTINUED)

CONTINUED:

> > > GEORGE (O.S)
>
> Hello?

INTERCUT between Erin in her car, and George in bed.

> > > ERIN
>
> I'm so tired I'm about to drive off the
> road. Keep me awake, willya?

> > > GEORGE
>
> What do you want, a joke?

> > > ERIN
>
> No.. Just tell me about your day. What
> went on back there?

> > > GEORGE
>
> Well, come to think of it, we did have a
> big event around here. Beth started
> talking.

> > > ERIN
>
> What?
> > > (beat)
> Beth? My Beth?

> > > GEORGE
>
> Yeah. We were sitting around at lunch and
> she pointed at a ball and said, "ball."
> Right out of the blue like that.

Erin says nothing, just stares out at the empty highway,
feeling all hollowed-out.

> > > GEORGE (cont'd)
>
> It was pretty intense. You know, seeing
> somebody's first word? All the words they
> say out of their life, that's the first
> word she says. She says "ball". She was
> pointing her little finger, with her
> beautiful, soft, chubby little arm. And
> her little cheeks. And she was lookin' at
> it, like she had been lookin' at it for
> nine months, you know, and just couldn't
> get it out but knowin' what it was. She
> didn't look away or anything. She was just
> sitting there with her arm out. You should
> have seen Matthew and Katie and me. Our
> jaws just dropped. And we're looking at
> her. I mean, we must have stood there for
> three or four minutes and just looked at
> her. And she just had her arm out, like
> that. You know? "Ball".
> > > (MORE)

CONTINUED: (2)

                    GEORGE (cont'd)
          And you know her little lips wrapped
          around her. It was great. It was intense.

Erin just nods. Keeps staring ahead as a tear rolls down her
cheek.

TITLE CARD:

NINE MONTHS LATER

EXT. HINKLEY BARBECUE - DAY

Open pits, pony rides, watermelon. George is watching Katie
and Matt being led around on ponies, an activity that stopped
being fun hours ago. Now they're just hot and tired.

BY THE BARBECUE, Ed is talking to an OLDER COUPLE as they
sign retainer agreements.

LATER...

Erin's trunk is open. She and Ed are clipping new clusters
of retainer agreements into the "PLAINTIFFS" binder.

LATER STILL...

Erin and Ed are passing out informational pamphlets.

A MAN (we later come to know him as CHARLES EMBRY) takes a
pamphlet and flirtatiously says;

                    CHARLES
          This got your phone number on it?

Erin blows him off with a laugh, barely registering his face.

                    ERIN
          I think there's more important information
          in there than that, trust me.

She sticks one in another hand before noticing that it's
George's.

                    GEORGE
          I'm bored, and so are the kids.

                    ERIN
          Well, I'm a little busy here, honey. I
          mean, we invited all these people here. Ed
          and I have to...

George starts to walk away.

                                              (CONTINUED)

CONTINUED:

>   ERIN (cont'd)
>   Okay, you know what. Can you take her?
>   She's getting heavy. And I can do my work
>   faster if you take her.

George drops the pamphlet and takes Beth from Erin. He heads
over to Matt and Katie, sitting glumly on a log.

LATER STILL...

Erin is heading over to George and the kids, ready to leave.

>   ERIN (cont'd)
>   Guess what?

>   GEORGE
>   What?

>   ERIN
>   I would like to go home.

>   GEORGE
>   Did you get everything done?

>   ERIN
>   Yeah, we got a lot of good work done.

>   GEORGE
>   I think I ate three watermelons.

>   ERIN
>   Three whole ones?

As Erin starts to leave, Donna comes up to her, with a MIDDLE-
AGED MAN in tow.

>   DONNA
>   Erin, this is Nelson Perez. He works over
>   at the compressor station -- PG&E.

>   PEREZ
>   Nice to meet you.

Erin stops in her tracks, very interested. But she can see,
out of the corner of her eye, that George and her kids are
getting impatient with her.

>   DONNA
>   I've come at a bad time.

>   ERIN
>   No, no, no. No.

(CONTINUED)

                         DONNA
          Maybe we'll just...

                         ERIN
          You know what? Just give me one second.

                         PEREZ
          We'll wait right over here.

She excuses herself for a moment and runs over to George.

                         ERIN
          Oh my God. You know what? Why don't you
          guys go ahead without me and I'll catch a
          ride with Ed.

                         MATTHEW
          No, ma!

                         ERIN
          No, no, no..I'll be right behind you. Be
          a good boy.

She gives each child a quick peck on the cheek, including
George. She runs back to Donna and the Middle Aged Man.
George is fuming. The kids are clearly disappointed.

                         GEORGE
          Come on kids..let's go.

In the stroller, Beth starts to whine. George reaches in his
pocket, finds her pacifier. As he's leaning down to give it
to her, he hears a RUMBLE coming down the street beyond the
barbecue area. The roar grows. He stands, looks.

A GROUP OF ABOUT TEN BIKERS ride by like thunder. He looks at
them, then at the stroller. George suddenly feels
ridiculous...and then guilty for feeling that way about the
kids..

Especially when Matthew reaches for his hand, squeezes it and
says, as if worried George will leave too.

The bikers REV LOUDLY as they ride by...then, fade away, pull
out. George just stands there and watches them go.

LATER STILL...

Erin and Perez are on a bench, talking. . Out of the corner of
her eye, she sees her car drive off.

                    ERIN
Mister Perez, this is so helpful. Is it
okay if I write some of this stuff down?

                    PEREZ
Sure.

                    ERIN
'Cause I have so many questions. I want
to know about how the plant works, and the
cooling towers, just everything...

                              DISSOLVE TO:

INT. ED'S OFFICE - DAY

His office is all about Hinkley. A map of the plume area and
a diagram of the plant cover one wall; photos of the plant
cover the credenza; piles of documents litter every surface.

Erin is up at the map, eating Chinese food.

                    ERIN
They used the hex chrom here, in these
cooling tanks, as an anti-corrosive. Then
they dumped the excess water here, in
these six ponds.

                    ED
I don't remember seeing any ponds up
there.

She bites into a forkful of food, keeps talking.

                    ERIN
Well, this is an old picture. They
covered 'em over. And not too carefully,
either, 'cause you dig one inch under the
surface, and the dirt is green as a
fucking shamrock.

                    ED
And that's what caused the contamination?

                    ERIN
It didn't help, but no. The real
problem's on the bottom.

She reaches for a document, reads from it.

CONTINUED:

> ERIN (cont'd)
> See, according to this, in most cases you
> would line the ponds so this shit couldn't
> seep into the ground. But guess what --

> ED
> They skipped that step.

> ERIN
> Mm-hm. And here are the ponds. The plume
> comes down like this. And Hinkley is down
> here. It's like fourteen years of hex
> chrom just flowing into the groundwater.

> ED
> Jesus..And this guy just offered all this
> information?

> ERIN
> Nelson cares what happens in those ponds
> 'cause he used to spend half his day
> wading in them. That was his job.

> ED
> No shit.

Ed smiles, but not enough. Erin notices.

> ERIN
> What's the matter?

Ed looks at her with an uncharacteristic vulnerability.

> ED
> I don't know if we can pull this off.

Erin knows how difficult that was for him to say...and she's
touched he felt he could say it to her.

> ED (cont'd)
> This is a monster case. We're up to four
> hundred and eleven plaintiffs, we've taken
> 162 declarations and there are probably
> hundreds more out there who have moved
> away, who are going to have to be
> found..and it's taking time and manpower
> and money's going out and nothing's coming
> in. I'm going to have to take a second
> mortgage on the house.

> ERIN
> So.

                          ED
                     (exasperated)
          "So"?
                     (beat)
          Look, I have to tell you, I've been making
          inquiries with other firms. Bigger firms
          to share some of the cost. They all said
          no. They say we don't have it.

                          ERIN
          Bullshit! We've got PG&E by the balls...

                          ED
          We've got PG&E Hinkley by the balls. But
          nobody's getting rich unless we can pin
          this on the corporate PG&E in San
          Fransisco.

                          ERIN
          What do you mean?

                          ED
          PG&E Corporate is claiming they had no way
          of knowing what was going on in Hinkley.

                          ERIN
          Oh, they knew. They had to know.

                          ED
          Show me the document that proves it.

She doesn't have one.

                          ED (cont'd)
          Then they didn't know. And if they didn't
          know, we can't hit 'em for punitive
          damages. And with punitive damages, we're
          talking about the kind of money that could
          actually have an effect on these people's
          lives...

She shoves her food away, knocking it over. Beat.

                          ERIN
          So what do we do?

                          ED
          Let's assume there are documents that
          connect PG&E Hinkley to PG&E Corporate.
          And they know these documents exist.
                     (MORE)

CONTINUED: (3)

                        ED (cont'd)
          We take our four hundred or so plaintiffs
          and everything you dug up and we file a
          lawsuit to provoke a reaction...to see if
          they offer a reasonable settlement or if
          they just throw more paper at us.

                        ERIN
                    (excited)
          Well, that sounds great! Let's do that!

Ed isn't finished.

                        ED
          There's a down side. PG&E will submit a
          demur - a list of reasons attacking each
          complaint, claiming each cause of action
          has no merit. And if the judge agrees with
          them, he'll dismiss our lawsuit and PG&E
          will have no reason to settle. Then it's
          all over.

                        ERIN
          So, basically, it's all up to what this
          one judge decides?

                        ED
          Basically, yeah.

                        ERIN
          Jesus.

They look at each other: Let's hope we get lucky.

EXT. PG&E STATION - NIGHT

Late, late at night. The plant is silent. The property seems
empty, until we notice Pete Jensen standing alone inside the
gates, staring up at the station.

After a beat, he picks up a rock and hurls it at the plant.
It misses. Not that it would do anything if it hit. He
reaches for another, throws it. Then another, and another.

He hurls rock after rock at the gigantic plant. Then,
overwhelmed by his impotence he lets out a TERRIFYING YELL.

INT. JENSEN'S HOUSE - DONNA'S BEDROOM - DAY

Donna' sitting quietly in bed. Erin is sitting on the edge
of the bed.

                        DONNA
          I'd got so used to having 'em come up
          benign, I guess I just didn't expect it.

CONTINUED:

She looks down her shirtfront.

>   DONNA (cont'd)
>   Sure wish I had longer to get used to the
>   idea.
>   (beat)
>   You think if you got no uterus, and no
>   breasts, you're still technically a woman?

>   ERIN
>   Sure you are. You're just a happier
>   woman, 'cause you don't have to deal with
>   maxi-pads and underwire.

Donna smiles a little. Then her face crumbles.

>   DONNA
>   We're gonna get them, aren't we, Erin?
>   You gotta promise me we're gonna get them.

INT. BARSTOW COURTROOM - DAY

Erin is sitting beside Ed on one side of the courtroom.

On the other side are the PG&E representatives, among them a
MS. SANCHEZ. These are the best lawyers money can buy, and
their demeanor says that winning isn't a goal, it's a forgone
conclusion. You'd much rather have them working for you than
against you.

JUDGE SIMMONS is at the bench, reviewing one last time, his
decision and the documents. Finally, he looks up;

>   JUDGE SIMMONS
>   All right.

Everyone pays attention.

>   JUDGE SIMMONS (cont'd)
>   I have before me a cause of action on
>   behalf of the residents of Hinkley,
>   California who wish to file a lawsuit
>   against Pacific Gas and Electric for
>   damages, medical expenses, personal trauma
>   due to the contamination of the
>   groundwater in their area by said
>   defendant. And I have here, a list of 84
>   motions to strike and demurs, submitted by
>   the representatives of Pacific Gas and
>   Electric, each one attacking and thereby
>   rejecting the validity of these
>   complaints. I have reviewed all the
>   information carefully.
>   (MORE)

CONTINUED:

                    JUDGE SIMMONS (cont'd)
        I am ready to give my decision. Before I
        do, is there anything anyone wants to say?

Ed grabs Erin's hand under the table, preventing her from
making a move. Erin submits.

                    ED
        No, your honor.

                    PG&E LAWYER
        No, your honor.

                    JUDGE SIMMONS
        Very well...In the case of the claimants
        of Hinkley California vs. Pacific Gas and
        Electric, it is the judgment of this court
        that each of the 84 motions to strike and
        demurs submitted by Pacific Gas and
        Electric be denied, and the cause of
        action against Pacific Gas and Electric be
        upheld...

Erin can hardly maintain her excitement. Ed squeezes her hand
harder. The PG&E people look sick.

                    JUDGE SIMMONS (cont'd)
        ...On a more personal note, as a resident
        here in Barstow, which is not far from
        Hinkley, I am...disturbed by evidence
        that suggests that not only was Hexavalent
        Chromium used, but your clients actually
        sent these residents pamphlets telling
        them it was good for them.

PG&E remain silent. The Judge stares at them, ending simply;

                    JUDGE SIMMONS (cont'd)
        Tell your clients they are going to trial.

INT. MASRY & VITITOE - RECEPTION - DAY

Talk about moving up the food chain. MS. SANCHEZ and the two
high-powered lawyers mill slowly about the reception area
like sharks. They all ooze importance.

INT. MASRY & VITITOE - OUTSIDE ED'S OFFICE - DAY

Erin, Ed, and Brenda are staring out at them.

                    ERIN
        Jesus. They look like the Secret Service.

CONTINUED:

                                ED
        Intimidation. Let the games begin.
                (then, to Brenda)
        Show them into the conference room.
                (gets an idea)
        Donald, Anna...I want to talk to you for a
        minute.

INT. MASRY & VITITOE - CONFERENCE ROOM - DAY

Sanchez and the two lawyers are seated.

The door opens and Ed enters, legal pad under his arm.
Followed by Erin, legal pad under her arm. Followed by Anna
(looking professional in Brenda's suit coat), legal pad under
her arm. Followed by Donald (in a suit produced from who
knows where), legal pad under his arm. If you didn't know
better, you'd assume it was a team of lawyers as well.

                                ED
        Counselors --

                            MS. SANCHEZ
        Counselors.

Ed and Erin sit down and get to work. Donald and Anna,
clearly told to just follow along, sit down a moment later.

INT. MASRY & VITITOE - CONFERENCE ROOM - LATER

Donald and Anna are sitting mutely in their seats beside Ed
and Erin, firing blank looks across the table.

                            SANCHEZ
        ...Let's be honest here. Twenty million
        dollars is more money than these people
        have ever dreamed of.

Erin has no patience for this today.

                            ERIN
        Oh, see, that pisses me off. First of all
        -- since the demur, we now have more than
        four hundred plaintiffs...and
                (mocking her)
        "let's be honest", we all know there's
        more out there. Now, they may not be the
        most sophisticated people, but they do
        know how to divide, and twenty million
        dollars isn't shit when it's split between
        them.

                                          (CONTINUED)

Donald and Anna exchange a look. This is getting
interesting.

                    ED
          Erin --

But there's no stopping her.

                    ERIN
          And second of all -- these people don't
          dream about being rich. They dream about
          being able to watch their kids swim in a
          pool without worrying that they'll have to
          have a hysterectomy at age 20, like Rosa
          Diaz -- a client of ours - or have their
          spine deteriorate like Stan Bloom, another
          client of ours.

Ed sits back now with a light smile, content to let Erin
continue.

                    ERIN (cont'd)
          So before you come back here with another
          lame-ass offer, I want you to think real
          hard about what your spine is worth, Mr.
          Walker -- or what you'd expect someone to
          pay you for your uterus, Ms. Sanchez --
          then you take out your calculator and
          multiply that number by a hundred.
          Anything less than that is a waste of our
          time.

Sanchez, throughout her speech, has been reacting in a
patronizing manner - as if Erin's words were of no import. By
the end of Erin's speech, Sanchez has picked up a glass of
water in front of her and is about to drink, when Erin says:

                    ERIN (cont'd)
          By the way, that water was brought in
          especially for you folks from a well in
          Hinkley...

Sanchez freezes, glass in hand. She is completely on the
spot. Erin may be bluffing - but can she risk it? Erin stares
her down. Sanchez slowly replaces the glass as she replies;

                    SANCHEZ
          I think this meeting is over.

                    ED
          Damn right it is.

(CONTINUED)

CONTINUED: (2)

Erin gets up and storms out first. We see on Anna's face, the first signs of respect for Erin.

EXT. ERIN'S HOUSE - FRONT STOOP - NIGHT

George is sitting alone on the stoop, drinking a beer. Music is coming from his house next door. He stares out into the street with a lot on his mind.

He sees Erin's car driving down the street, on her way home. He rises and enters the house.

INT. ERIN'S HOUSE - ERIN'S BEDROOM - NIGHT

George is sitting on the bed when Erin enters.

> ERIN
> Look at this. What the fuck, George? Did a bomb blow up? You letting the kids run wild?

He doesn't answer. Doesn't move. She notices this. He's very calm. He holds out a small box of earrings.

> ERIN (cont'd)
> What's that?

> GEORGE
> I saw 'em in the mall one day, and I thought damn, those would look good on those beautiful ears. So I bought 'em. And I said to myself, next time Erin says something nice, does something nice, I'll surprise her with 'em.
> (beat)
> Know how long ago that was? Six months.

> ERIN
> I'm sorry. I'm just working so hard --

> GEORGE
> (stands)
> And what I'm thinking is, you oughta either find a different job or a different guy. 'Cause there may be men who don't mind being the maid and getting nothing in return, but I'm sure as shit ain't one of 'em.

> ERIN
> I can't leave my job, George.

CONTINUED:

> GEORGE
> Yeah, you can. You could just quit.
> People do it all the time.

> ERIN
> How can you ask me to do that? This job --
> For the first time in my life, I got
> people respecting me. Up in Hinkley, I
> walk into a room and everyone shuts up
> just to hear what I got to say. I never
> had that. Ever. Don't ask me to give it
> up.

> GEORGE
> And what about what your kids are giving
> up?

> ERIN
> Look, I'm doing a lot better for those
> kids now than I did living with my
> parents. One day they'll understand that.

> GEORGE
> And what about me?

> ERIN
> What about you? you think either one of
> the men who gave me those children asked
> what I wanted before they walked away?!
> All I've ever done is bend my life around
> what men decided they need! Well not now.
> I'm sorry. I won't do it.

> GEORGE
> I'm not them. What more do I have to do to
> prove that?

For a moment, Erin is stymied...then, softly;

> ERIN
> Stay.

He lowers his head, then stands, to leave. He too speaks
gently;

> GEORGE
> What for? You got a raise. You can afford
> day care.....You don't need me.

Erin feels caught between two truths - what she feels for
George..and what she feels for her new life.

(CONTINUED)

CONTINUED: (2)

George walks to her, kisses her on the cheek and holds her hands...Then exits..

Erin looks in her hands - where George has placed the velvet jewelry box of earrings...

INT. HYUNDAI - DAY

Erin is driving, looking weary. Her kids are in the car. No one is speaking. An angry Matthew sits sullenly looking out the window. Beth is asleep. Matthew suddenly shuts off the radio.

Erin drives, bothered by his actions but consumed with her own thoughts...The family feels divided..each in their own world.

EXT. PAMELA DUNCAN'S HOUSE - DAY

Pamela, smoking a cigarette, opens the front door to find Erin there, with her kids, holding a box of cake. Pamela raises her eyebrow.

INT. PAMELA DUNCAN'S HOUSE - DAY

The kids are seen through the window, playing outside - Matthew, reluctantly.

Pamela and Erin are finishing coffee, cake, stories..

                    ERIN
          We can get them, Pamela. We can.

                    PAMELA
          I don't want to feel it all over again and
          then...not have it come out right. I don't
          know if I could handle that. Put my kids
          through that.

                    ERIN
          See, the thing is...it doesn't matter if
          you win lose or draw here. You were lied
          to. You're sick, your kids are sick
          because of those lies. If for no other
          reason, you all have to come together to
          stand up in a courtroom and say that.

                    PAMELA
          I'd bring the kids into the hospital with
          towels soaked from their nosebleeds. They
          called county services because they
          assumed the kids were being abused.

                                        (CONTINUED)

CONTINUED:

Erin has her.

EXT. MASRY & VITITOE PARKING LOT - DAY

The Hyundai pulls into the lot. We hear voices from within
the car, arguing;

INT. ERIN'S HYUNDAI - DAY

Erin is with her kids. She and Matthew are fighting;

> ERIN
> Am I going to get the best behavior I was
> talking about earlier, in the office?

> MATTHEW
> No.

> ERIN
> What's with the attitude? I just need
> cool, I need quiet. Okay? Hello? Am I
> alone in the car?

EXT. MASRY & VITITOE PARKING LOT - DAY

Erin carries Beth as she continues to fight with Matthew.

> MATTHEW
> ...why everything has to be
> such a big deal. All I want
> to do is play roller hockey
> Other moms give permission.

> ERIN
> ...all I'm saying is, we'll
> see. I can't talk about this
> now. I don't care what other
> moms do.

> MATTHEW
> (annoyed)
> ..So when!? When can I get a friggin
> answer!?

> ERIN
> Don't talk to me like that!

> MATTHEW
> Randy's mom said yes right away!!

> ERIN
> (snapping)
> Well, goddamn it, Matthew -- Randy's mom
> doesn't work and Randy's dad didn't leave
> her, so figuring out who's gonna drive who
> to roller hockey every other week is a
> little easier over at Randy's house. Now
> cool it.

INT. MASRY & VITITOE - WAITING ROOM - DAY

Erin carries Beth, followed by Matthew and Katie. She sits
the two older children down.

                    ERIN
          I'll be as quick as I can, all right?
          Watch your sister.

Matthew ignores her..

                    ERIN (cont'd)
          Matthew..

                    MATTHEW
               (snaps at her)
          ALRIGHT! FINE!

Rosalind looks up. Erin decides not to respond. She enters
the main room.

INT. MASRY & VITITOE - MAIN ROOM - DAY

As she passes by the CONFERENCE ROOM, she sees;

Ed shaking hands and taking a check from a snazzy lawyer
type. Suspicious, she enters;

INT. CONFERENCE ROOM - DAY

Ed sees Erin and makes introductions;

                    ED
          Erin! I was just taking about you. I want
          you to meet our new partner, Kurt Potter.
          He'll be handling Hinkley now.

                    POTTER
               (to Ed)
          Now I know what you meant by a secret
          weapon.
               (to Erin)
          Erin, it's great to meet you. You've done
          a fabulous job.
               (to Ed)
          I'll be seeing you.

                    ED
          Thanks. I appreciate your coming over.

He blows out of the room. Erin glares at Ed.

(CONTINUED)

CONTINUED:

                         ED
            What?

                         ERIN
            Our new partner? When was I gonna find out
            - in the monthly newsletter?

                         ED
            Hey..just listen. Did I ever tell you
            about the airline case?

                         ERIN
            Airline case!? What the fuck are you
            talking about?

                         ED
                    (patient)
            A few years back I was trying this airline
            case and I got my ass kicked by this guy -
            he just smothered me in paper. Brutal.
            This guy was the toughest mother I'd ever
            been up against.

                         ERIN
            Jesus, make a point.

                         ED
            It was Kurt Potter! When we got the PG&E
            decision from the judge, I called him and
            asked him to partner. He didn't hesitate.

                         ERIN
            Well, of course NOW he wouldn't hesitate.
            We did all the fucking work. Where was he
            before?

                         ED
            Doesn't matter..Erin, listen to me - it
            doesn't matter. You want to win this?
                    (shows her the check)
            He just gave me this check. It covers all
            our expenses to date. The whole thing.
            He's got more toxic tort experience than
            anyone in the state. This is good news.

Erin rises, still not happy about it - feeling like she's
being pushed out. She drops the check on the table and exits,
stopping by the door to say, as if without, any importance;

                         ERIN
            By the way...I got Pamela Duncan.

She exits before Ed can say "Great - good work!"..

INT. ERIN'S HOUSE - KITCHEN - DAY

Erin is standing at the sink, visibly exhausted, trying to do
the dinner dishes with one arm and comfort Beth, who's
CRYING, with the other. Matthew comes in and runs into his
room, slamming the door.

Erin hears a motorcycle revving up. She walks to the front
door and looks out to see:

GEORGE riding away. At the same time, a MESSENGER is walking
up her front walk. Erin opens the door as he approaches;

                    MESSENGER
          Erin Brockovich?

                    ERIN
          Yeah?

                    MESSENGER
          Package from Masry and Vititoe.

He hands her a manila envelope. She signs for the package,
then tears into it as the Messenger heads away.

A CHECK and a SET OF KEYS fall out. She looks at the check.
It's made out for $5,000. A note attached reads "HIRE A
NANNY. LOOK OUTSIDE. AND CHEER THE FUCK UP! - ED."

Erin looks up and sees a BRAND NEW CHEVY BLAZER parked on the
curb. She looks at the keys in her hand. Chevy keys.

EXT. POTTER, HUGHES & ROSEWOOD - DAY

The top floors of an impressive skyscraper in downtown L.A.

INT. POTTER, HUGHES & ROSEWOOD - CONFERENCE ROOM - DAY

Potter, Ed, Erin, THERESA, and a few PARALEGALS are sitting
around the table. As the conversation ping-pongs between Ed
and Potter, Potter completely ignores Erin.

                    POTTER
          ...PG&E have requested we go to binding
          arbitration...

                    ERIN
          What's that?

Everyone is surprised by her honest lack of knowledge. She
doesn't give a shit.

                                          (CONTINUED)

                         POTTER
          We try the case without a jury, just a
          judge. They call it a test trial, and the
          judge's decision is final, there's no
          appeal. How many plaintiffs do you have?

                         ERIN
          634.

                         POTTER
          Well, they won't try that many at once, so
          we get them in groups of twenty to thirty,
          the worst cases - the ones who are clearly
          the sickest, most life threatened - are in
          the first group and so on...and each gets
          to go before the judge to determine
          damages. PG&E have proposed they are
          liable from anywhere between fifty and
          four hundred million.

Erin and Ed exchange looks. Erin is uneasy.

                         ERIN
          Wait a minute. Let me get this straight.

                         ED
          Erin, if we went to trial, PG&E could
          stretch this over ten years, with appeal
          after appeal...

                         ERIN
          But these people are expecting a trial.
          That's what we told them. You and me. They
          won't understand this.

                         ED
          Kurt thinks it's the best way to go.

Potter starts talking as we focus on Erin's expression - her
realization that all of this has already been decided without
her.

                         POTTER
          I promise you, we'll be very sensitive on
          this point. We'll make sure they
          understand it's the only way to go forward
          at this time. But we have a lot of work to
          do before we even broach the subject.

Theresa sees impatience brewing, tries to intercede.

CONTINUED: (2)

> THERESA
> You know what? Why don't I take Erin down
> the hall, so we can start on this stuff
> and I'll fill her in on the rest..

> ERIN
> Hey -- those are my files --

> THERESA
> Yeah, we had them couriered over. And
> listen, good work. They're a great start.
> We're just going to have to spend a little
> time filling in the holes in your
> research.

Okay, these people are starting to piss her off.

> ERIN
> Excuse me - Theresa, was it? There are no
> holes in my research.

> THERESA
> No offense. There are just some things we
> need to know that you probably didn't know
> to ask.

> ERIN
> Don't talk to me like I'm an idiot, okay?
> I may not have a law degree, but I've
> spent 18 months on this case, and I know
> more about those plaintiffs than you ever
> will.

> THERESA
> Erin. You don't even have phone numbers
> for some of them.

> ERIN
> Whose number do you need?

> THERESA
> Everyone's. This is a lawsuit. We need
> to be able to contact the plaintiffs.

> ERIN
> I said, <u>whose number do you need</u>?

> THERESA
> You don't know six hundred plaintiffs'
> numbers by heart.

Erin just stares at her. Theresa sighs, reluctantly glances
down at a file.

(CONTINUED)

                              THERESA (cont'd)
                    Annabelle Daniels.

                              ERIN
                    Annabelle Daniels.   714-454-9346.

As Theresa starts to write it down;

                              ERIN (cont'd)
                    10 years old, 11 in May. Lived on the
                    plume since birth. Wanted to be a
                    synchronized swimmer, so she spent every
                    minute she could in the PG&E pool. She
                    had a tumor in her brain stem detected
                    last November, had an operation on
                    Thanksgiving, shrunk it with radiation
                    after that. Her parents are Rita and Ted.
                    Ted's got Crohn's disease, and Rita has
                    chronic headaches and nausea and underwent
                    a hysterectomy last fall. Ted grew up in
                    Hinkley. His brother Robbie and his wife
                    May and their five kids, Robbie, Jr.,
                    Martha, Ed, Rose, and Peter lived on the
                    plume too. Their number's 454-9554. You
                    want their diseases?

Beat. Erin glares at Theresa, indignant.

                              THERESA
                    Okay, look -- I think we got off on the
                    wrong foot here --

                              ERIN
                    That's all you got, lady. Two wrong feet
                    in fucking ugly shoes.

INT. PARKING LOT - NIGHT

Erin is following Ed to his car. He's furious.

                              ERIN
                    She insulted me!

                              ED
                    Bullshit. It was a misunderstanding. But
                    instead of handling it politely, instead
                    of treating her with respect, you insult
                    her.

                              ERIN
                    Why the fuck should I respect her?

Ed stops in his tracks, furious. He glares at her.

                                                          (CONTINUED)

CONTINUED:

                         ED
          Look! Just because she's not supporting
          three kids with no husband and no
          education, doesn't make her an idiot!
          Just because she dresses like a lawyer,
          doesn't mean she didn't work her ass off
          in law school and shit positions to earn
          her way.

                         ERIN
          Well excuse me for not going to law
          school.

                         ED
          Law school! At this point, I'd settle for
          charm school!

On that, he gets in the car, slams the door, and drives off.

EXT. LINWOOD DAIRY - DAY

Bob Linwood is in his barn, mucking it out. Theresa is at
the edge of the property, trying unsuccessfully to get his
attention by yelling and waving her arms. In her expensive
shoes, she's stopped short of the cow patty minefield.

INT. POTTER, HUGHES & ROSEWOOD - CONFERENCE ROOM - DAY

CLOSE ON A CLIENT FILE as a hand fills in a phone number.

WIDEN TO SEE Erin seated with a PARALEGAL, rattling off facts
and numbers from memory. She's seized by a COUGHING FIT.

INT. DANIELS' HOUSE - DAY

Theresa is talking to Rita and Ted Daniels. Annabelle is
curled up on the sofa, wrapped in a blanket. Rita and Ted
notice that Theresa doesn't even look at Annabelle.

INT. ERIN'S HOUSE - KITCHEN - DAY

Erin is lying in bed, home sick, talking on the phone. She's
talking over the noise to TANIA, her 20-something Eastern
European nanny, vacuuming the hall.

                         ERIN
          ..I know Theresa isn't real warm, but they
          say she's a real good lawyer...

INT. DANIELS' HOUSE - DAY

Ted Daniels is on the Phone. Rita is next to him.

                                                  (CONTINUED)

CONTINUED:

                        TED
          She's asking the same questions you asked.
          We already told you everything. I don't
          want her coming to the house again. She's
          kinda stuck up, and she upsets Annabelle.

                        ERIN
                   (on her cell phone)
          If you don't like Theresa, that's okay.
          And you know how important Annabelle is to
          me. Me and Ed are still here for you.

                        TED
          I called Ed two days ago, Erin, and he
          still hasn't called me back. Now, I hate
          to say this, but everyone's pretty upset
          about that arbitration thing...

                        ERIN
                   (stunned)
          WHAT?

                        TED
          I mean, Pamela's written a letter in the
          Hinkley news telling everybody to get new
          lawyers..that we've been lied to.

Erin is breathless with rage.

                        TED (cont'd)
          Is it true?

                        ERIN
                   (stammers)
          No.

                        TED
          Did you?

                        ERIN
          I'm telling you the truth, and I will get
          to the bottom of all of this.

                        TED
          Don't lie to us.

INT. MASRY & VITITOE - CONFERENCE ROOM - DAY

Ed and Theresa are listening to Potter; :

(CONTINUED)

CONTINUED:

                          POTTER
              ...I'm not saying it's not a strong case.
              If it wasn't a strong case, every demur
              wouldn't have been dismissed and I
              wouldn't be here. What I am saying is, we
              still don't have our smoking gun that ties
              Hinkley to San Fransisco - it could be a
              document, a person, but it's something
              that proves that prior to 1987, PG&E
              corporate knew there was something wrong
              with the water in Hinkley and did nothing
              about it.

INT. MASRY & VITITOE - RECEPTION - DAY

Erin drags herself into the office.

                          ROSALIND
              Hey, Erin, I thought you were taking a
              sick day.

                          ERIN
              So did I.

She heads toward Ed's office, but stops when she sees the
meeting in progress in the conference room. Ed is on the
side of the table facing her, flanked by Potter and Theresa.

                          ERIN (cont'd)
              What's going on in there?

                          ROSALIND
              Meeting about the PG&E thing.

                          ERIN
              PG& -- Are you sure?

                          ROSALIND
              Yup.

Erin feels this like a sock in the gut. She stares at the
meeting, stunned.

INT. MASRY & VITITOE - CONFERENCE ROOM - DAY

At that point, Ed looks beyond Potter to see...

Erin staring at him from the other side of the glass wall,
her face cold with hurt and anger.

                          ED
              Could I -- just take a brief break here
              for a moment? I'll be right back.

CONTINUED:

He gets up and goes out into:

INT. MASRY & VITITOE - MAIN ROOM - DAY

Ed comes out. Erin's so angry she can barely breathe.

                    ERIN
          What are you fucking doing?!

                    ED
          We're just having a meeting.

                    ERIN
          If you tell me to relax, I'm gonna choke
          you with that fucking tie.

                    ED
          You told me you weren't feeling great. i
          wanted you to rest.

                    ERIN
          Bullshit. You'd drag me off my deathbed
          if if helped you.
                    (weakened)
          How could you take this away from me?

                    ED
          No one's taking anything, will you listen
          to me-

                    ERIN
          Bullshit. You stuck me in Siberia
          dictating to some goddamn steno clerk so
          you could finish this thing without me.

                    ED
          Erin, they screwed up!
                    (Erin shuts up)
          Do I have your attention now? They screwed
          up and they admit it.

Beat.

                    ED (cont'd)
          The arbitration proposal they sent might
          as well have been written in Sanskrit for
          all the sense it made to anyone in
          Hinkley.

                    ERIN
          I know. I spoke to Ted. Pamela Duncan
          wouldn't even get on the phone with me.

CONTINUED:

                    ED
     Pamela's got everybody seeing red with
     that letter she wrote to the press. She
     called us thieves. And they're all
     listening to her. This whole thing is
     about to fall apart Erin.

                    ERIN
     Why?

                    ED
     Because in order to even go to arbitration
     - we have to get the plaintiffs to
     agree...

                    ERIN
     How many?

                    ED
     Usually you can manage to get about 70
     percent. PG&E are demanding we get
     ninety. In other words, everybody. This is
     serious now, Erin. Do you understand?

                    ERIN
     And, what Ed, I'm not serious?

                    ED
     You're emotional. You're erratic. You
     say any goddamn thing that comes into your
     head. You make this personal and it
     isn't.

                    ERIN
     Not personal? That's my work in there. My
     sweat, my time away from my kids... If
     that's not personal, I don't know what is.

She starts to COUGH AND CRUMBLE, but fights it.

                    ED
     Now go home. Get well. Because you're no
     good to me sick.
               (then, admits)
     I need you. All right? This case needs
     you.

Beat. Then Erin asks him, referring to Potter and Theresa:

                    ERIN
     Did you tell them that?

Clearly, Ed has not. She looks at him with disappointment, hurt and exhaustion. She turns and walks away.

EXT. HINKLEY FIREHOUSE - NIGHT

The lot is filling with cars and trucks; headlights crisscross each other as people pull in from all directions. It is a stifling hot evening.

INT. HINKLEY FIREHOUSE - LATER

It's sweltering. The room, packed with plaintiffs, hums with horse flies and tension. People are fanning themselves with the release forms. Ed's addressing them from a raised platform.

                    ED
          ..Binding arbitration isn't all that
          different from a trial. It's overseen by
          a judge. Evidence is presented in much
          the same way...

                    PLAINTIFF (O.S.)
          And then a jury decides?

                    ED
          No, sorry, I should have mentioned that.
          There's no jury in binding arbitration.
          No jury, no appeal.

                    BOB LINWOOD
          So what are our options if we don't like
          the result?

                    ED
          Well -- you have none. The judge's
          decision is final. But we really don't
          anticipate that being a problem...

Unhappy murmuring in the crowd. Now, in addition to the stifling heat, the large room is thick with mistrust. People are shifting in their seats, whispering to each other.

                    ED (cont'd)
          As I said before, it will <u>definitely</u> be
          somewhere between 50 and 400 million
          dollars...

                    MANDY ROBINSON
          Which? There's a big difference there.

CONTINUED:

                    ED
          I wouldn't want to speculate at this
          point.

More whispering, more movement.

                    MANDY ROBINSON
          How does it get divided?

                    PLAINTIFF
          Yeah, who gets what? My medical bills
          started two years before some other people
          here.

                    RITA DANIELS
          But my kid's been in and out of the
          hospital a lot more than his. It shouldn't
          matter when it started.

                    ED
          Wait a minute, that's not-

The crowd erupts. The GRUMBLE of discontent has overtaken the
room. Erin watches the meeting fall apart. It's driving her
crazy. She notices CHARLES EMBRY, the flirty guy from the
picnic, watching her from the rear of the room. His smile is
hard to interpret.

                    ED (cont'd)
          ...People, listen, please..the point we
          want to address tonight is getting
          everyone to agree that going binding
          arbitration is preferable to a trial that
          could go on for ten years before you see
          any money.

                    PLAINTIFF
          Well, maybe some of us want to go ten
          years.

                    OTHER PLAINTIFFS
                 (overlaps)
          I don't..YEAH!...Speak for yourself!..This
          is bullshit!!!Let him talk, for Christ's
          Sake...!!

                    ED
                 (overlaps)
          We have to agree or no one has a chance...

Some people are getting up to leave.

                        ED (cont'd)
                     (emphatic)
          ...for those of you about to leave, I'd
          like you to keep this date in mind: 1978.
          That's the year of the Love Canal
          controversy, and those people are still
          waiting for their money. Think about where
          you'll be in fifteen or twenty years.

The people that were leaving stop.

                        ED (cont'd)
          Look. Everyone. Is this a big decision?
          Absolutely. But I do not believe - and I
          wouldn't say this otherwise - I do not
          believe this is a sell-out.
                     (beat)
          This is the best shot at getting everyone
          some money now. You and I both know that
          some people in this room can't afford to
          wait, to take that chance. Are you going
          to make them wait?

The crowd is listening now.

                                        DISSOLVE TO:

INT. FIREHOUSE - LATER THAT NIGHT

The last car drives away. The clock reads 12:35 AM. Erin and
Ed are counting the agreements signed by those who wish to
continue with the arbitration - talking, counting as we;

                        ED
          ...So how many all together..

                        ERIN
          Well, we got just about everybody who came
          here tonight. But that still leaves us
          about a hundred and fifty short.

                        ED
          Shit.

                        ERIN
          We're going to have to go door-to-door Ed.
                     (beat)
          I gotta go pick up my kids.

                        ED
          You need a hand with that?

CONTINUED:

                         ERIN
              No.

He nods. Erin looks at him.

                         ERIN (cont'd)
              You did good, Ed.

                         ED
              We'll see.

EXT. HINKLEY MOTEL - DAY

Very early. Erin is visible in the motel office, talking to
the clerk, when George's motorcycle pulls into the parking
lot.

EXT. ERIN"S MOTEL ROOM - DAY

Erin comes up to him, hands him a key.

                         ERIN
              Thanks for coming.

He takes it, glances toward the motel room.

                         ERIN (cont'd)
                    (awkward beat)
              Look, don't take any of 'em on your bike,
              okay? Call a cab if you wanna go
              somewhere.

She hands him a wad of cash. He hands it back.

                         GEORGE
              I have money...How long's this whole thing
              gonna take?

                         ERIN
              I don't know. Few days. I got you your
              own room.

George is engaged in an action throughout Erin's speech -
locking up his bike, getting his stuff - never looking at
her..

                         ERIN (cont'd)
              I am really sorry, George.

                         GEORGE
              Have the kids eaten?

                                              (CONTINUED)

CONTINUED:

                              ERIN
              No.

George turns and walks into the motel. Erin gets into the
truck and pulls out.

EXT. HINKLEY - COMMUNITY BOULEVARD - DAY

Erin's Chevy is bombing down the road.

INT/EXT. HINKLEY - DAY

Erin and Ed go door-to-door. Together and separately they
meet people in their kitchens, porches, garages, and
driveways in order to get them signed up.

INT. ERIN'S MOTEL ROOM - NIGHT

In the wee hours. While her kids sleep, Erin sits at the
cheap motel room table, going through her forms, organizing,
alphabetizing.

We notice TWO BOXES - one is labeled, SIGNED RELEASE
FORMS..the other, UNSIGNED RELEASE FORMS. The box marked
"unsigned" is fuller.

INT. ERIN'S MOTEL ROOM - DAY

CLOSE ON ERIN, fast asleep a the table, her face pressed
against the linoleum. There's some NOISE in the room,
WHISPERING. Erin stirs and looks around to see George behind
her, diapering Beth, while Matt and Katie put their shoes on.

                              ERIN
              What time is it?

                              GEORGE
              Real early. We're just gonna take your
              car to get some breakfast.

Erin forces herself awake.

                              ERIN
              No, I need my car --

                              GEORGE
              We'll just be a minute. Get a little more
              sleep.

He picks up Beth, takes Katie's hand, and calls across the
room to Matthew.

                                                    (CONTINUED)

CONTINUED:

> GEORGE (cont'd)
> C'mon pal. Leave that alone, we gotta go.

Erin turns to see Matthew holding one of her release forms.

> ERIN
> Oh, baby, please don't play with that,
> okay? I got 'em all organized. Just put it
> back.

But he's reading it. And something has caught his attention.
He looks up at Erin.

> MATTHEW
> This girl's the same age as me.

Erin gently takes the form away from Matthew, wanting to
shield him from the harsh realities of this case.

> ERIN
> That's right, sweetheart.

She replaces the form on top of the stack.

> MATTHEW
> She's one of the sick people?

> ERIN
> Yeah. She is.
> (beat)
> But you know what? That's why I'm helping
> her. So she can get some medicine to make
> her feel better.

Matthew mulls this over a bit more.

> MATTHEW
> How come her own mom isn't helping her?

> ERIN
> 'Cause her own mom's real sick, too.

Matthew thinks real hard about this, then heads over to the
door, where George, Beth, and Katie are waiting for him.
Before he leaves, though, he turns back to Erin.

> MATTHEW
> Maybe we'll bring you back some breakfast.
> You want eggs?

She looks at Matthew and her eyes fill with tears. She is so
proud of her son in this moment. As if his understanding is
what she needed all along.

(CONTINUED)

                            ERIN
           Eggs'd be great, baby. Eggs'd be perfect.

INT/EXT. HINKLEY - DAY

Erin continues meeting plaintiffs, collecting signatures.
She drops more forms into the "signed" box.

EXT. PAMELA DUNCAN'S HOUSE - DAY

Erin is on her doorstep once more. Pamela opens the door,
cautiously.

INT. THE BACK OF ERIN'S TRUCK - NIGHT

The signed stack has grown; the unsigned stack has shrunk.
Erin drops five more agreements into the "signed" box.

EXT. LOST CAUSE SALOON - NIGHT

Erin's truck drives into the parking lot. As she brings the
vehicle to a halt, some of the signed documents slide to the
floor. She picks them up.

INT. LOST CAUSE SALOON - NIGHT

Erin enters and crosses to the counter. The BARTENDER
approaches her.

                            ERIN
           Hey, Matt.

                        BARTENDER
           Hey, Erin. How are you?

                            ERIN
           Good. How are you?

                        BARTENDER
           Have you been at this all day?

                            ERIN
           Yeah.

                        BARTENDER
           Well, you look tired. Do you want some
           coffee?

                            ERIN
           I'd love some.

                        BARTENDER
           I'll make a fresh pot.

CONTINUED:

A man approaches Erin at the bar.

                    CHARLES EMBRY
          Say, don't I know you?

She looks up at him. It's the strange guy in the baseball hat
from the barbecue and the town meeting.

                    ERIN
                    (lying)
          I don't think so.

                    EMBRY
          Sure. You were at that barbecue in
          Hinkley. Handing out stuff. And the town
          meeting.

                    ERIN
          Mmm.

                    EMBRY
          I was watching you. I had my eye on you...

                    ERIN
          Oh...nice..

                    EMBRY
          I saw ya...saw ya talking to
          everybody..writing stuff down...I said to
          myself..something about her..I really like
          that girl.

                    ERIN
                    (to bartender)
          Matt, can I get that coffee to go?

                    BARTENDER
          Sure.

He gets her a styrofoam cup.

                    EMBRY (cont'd)
          I feel like I could talk to you, like
          you're a person I can say anything to...

Erin smiles, impatient to get her coffee and get out.

                    ERIN
          What do I owe you?

                    BARTENDER
          There's no charge.

                              ERIN
                    Thanks, Matt.
                              (to Embry)
                    Well, nice talking to you.

Embry leans in. Erin really wants to get out of here.

                              EMBRY
                    Would it be important to you if I told you
                    that when I worked at the Hinkley plant, I
                    destroyed documents?

Erin stares blankly. She forgets to breathe. Her mind races.

                              ERIN
                    Maybe...
                              (doesn't know his name)
                    What did you say your name was?

                              EMBRY
                    Charles Embry.

                              ERIN
                    Charles...Nice to meet you. Would
                    you..would you excuse me a moment - I just
                    have to go to the bathroom.

She calmly exits OS.

                                                        CUT TO:

EXT. LOST CAUSE SALOON - NIGHT

Erin runs her ass off to her truck...opens the door, searches
for her cell phone...

                              ERIN
                    Oh, come on! You fucking piece of <u>crap</u>
                    with no signal! Fuck!

She spots a pay phone.

INT. ED'S OFFICE - NIGHT

Ed's working. The phone rings.

                              ED
                    Yeah?..What?

INTERCUT ERIN

                    ERIN
Ed, oh my God! This guy! Charles! He said
that he destroyed records. He worked at
Hinkley..

                    ED
Slow down, slow down.

                    ERIN
No. I'm just trying to relax, and this
guy, this Charles Embry guy.

                    ED
Who?

                    ERIN
Charles Embry. First I thought he was
trying to kill me, but then I thought he
was trying to pick me up, and, I don't
know, maybe he is. By why would he say
that? Why would he use that as his line? I
mean, it's crazy.

Ed rises out of his chair as he listens..

                    ED
Shit..Look, go back and see if he'll make
a declaration.

                    ERIN
A declaration...

                    ED
But be careful. Don't scare him off.

                    ERIN
Okay...

                    ED
And stay calm. Just remember, if it
weren't for you I'd be in Palm Springs
right now. You're good at talking people
into things.
                    (Erin smiles at the
                     compliment)
Don't pepper him with too many questions.
People want to tell their stories..Just
let him talk. Let him do all the talking,
all right?

                              ERIN
                    Okay.

                                                   CUT BACK TO:

INT. LOST CAUSE SALOON - NIGHT

A deliberately calm Erin talks to Charles;

                              ERIN
                    Sorry. Would you like another beer?

                              EMBRY
                    No.

Long beat. Erin waits. Charles just stares at her. She is
about to ask a question but stops herself. Then:

                              EMBRY (cont'd)
                    My cousin passed away yesterday. He had
                    kidney tumors, no colon - his intestines
                    were eaten out. Forty-one years old. I
                    just remember seeing him over at the
                    plant, draining the cooling towers,
                    wearing one of those - what do you call
                    'em - doctor masks - and it'd be soaked
                    red from the nose bleeds.

INT. LOST CAUSE SALOON - LATER THAT NIGHT

Erin and Charles are the only patrons. Erin's eating peanuts
from a bowl. Charles has a beer.

                              EMBRY
                    I was working in the compressor, and out
                    of nowhere the supervisor calls me up to
                    the office and says, we're gonna give you
                    a shredder machine, and send you on down
                    to the warehouse. We want you to get rid
                    of all the documents we got stored there.

                              ERIN
                    Did he say why?

                              EMBRY
                    Nope. And I didn't ask.

                              ERIN
                    Did you get a look at the stuff you
                    destroyed?

                         EMBRY
          There was a lot of dull stuff -- vacation
          schedules, the like.
                    (beat)
          But then there were a few memos about the
          holding ponds. The water in them. They
          had readings from test wells, stuff like
          that.

                         ERIN
          And you were told to destroy those?

                         EMBRY
          That's right.

Erin plays it down, takes a sip of beer. Charles smiles;

                         EMBRY (cont'd)
          Course, as it turns out, I'm not a very
          good employee.

Erin stops. She looks at him. She raises a glass of beer and
they toast the moment.

INT. POTTER, HUGHES & ROSEWOOD - RECEPTION - DAY

Erin and Ed enter, with boxes in their arms and a whole lot
of attitude.

INT. POTTER, HUGHES & ROSEWOOD - CONFERENCE ROOM - DAY

The table is covered with boxes of documents: the anticipated
slew of paper that PG&E is sending them. Kurt, Theresa, and
about FIVE PARALEGALS are sifting through them.

Erin and Ed breeze in like sunshine.

                         ERIN
          Morning!

                         POTTER
          Erin? Ed? What's this --

                         ERIN
                    (to Ed)
          May I?

                         ED
          Go ahead.

                         ERIN
          You know what, Mr. Potter? We completely
          forgot your birthday this year.
                    (MORE)

                                                      (CONTINUED)

CONTINUED:

                    ERIN (cont'd)
       And seeing as how you've been so good to
       me, it seemed a terrible oversight. So
       what Ed and I have been doing over the
       last few days is putting together a
       present for you.

She plunks the box down on the table. Potter opens the top of
the box. Looks in.

                    ERIN (cont'd)
       634, They're all signed. Every single
       one.

Potter, Theresa, et al...are stunned.

                    THERESA
       Ho - ly - shit.

                    ERIN
       Oh, now don't get all jealous, Theresa.
           (to Ed)
       She's getting a little jealous.
           (to Theresa)
       We got a little something for you, too.

Erin hands Theresa a manila envelope. She opens it.

                    ERIN (cont'd)
       Internal PG&E documents, all about the
       contamination. The one I like best says,
       and I'm paraphrasing here, but it says
       yes, the water's poisonous, but it'd be
       better for all involved if this matter
       wasn't discussed with the neighbors. It's
       to the Hinkley station, from PG&E
       Headquarters. Stamped received, March,
       1966.

Potter and Theresa reel. Ed shakes his head in disbelief.

                    POTTER
       Where did -- how did you do this?

                    ERIN
       Well, seeing as I have no brains or legal
       expertise, and Ed here was losing all
       faith in the system...am I right?...

                    ED
       Oh yes..completely..No faith..

                        ERIN
          I just went on up there and performed
          sexual favors. 634 blow jobs in five
          days. I'm really quite tired.

Ed's head falls to his chest - he didn't know that was
coming. But Erin just smiles...digesting her canary.

                                        DISSOLVE TO:

EXT. HIGHWAY - DAY

Erin's Chevy glides across the desert landscape. Inside,
George is at the wheel. Time has passed -- Erin's hair is a
little different.

                        GEORGE
          I'm still not sure why you wanted me to
          come.

                        ERIN
          I want you to see what you've helped to
          do.

EXT. JENSEN'S HOUSE - DAY

Donna is working in her garden. The sound of a car
approaching turns her head, and when she recognizes Erin's
vehicle, she rises in anticipation.

Erin and George exit the Chevy and walk to the house.

                        DONNA
          Hi.

                        ERIN
          Hi. How you feeling today?

                        DONNA
          Good. It's a good day.

                        ERIN
          I'm glad.

                        DONNA
          Well, come on. What a nice surprise this
          is.

EXT. JENSEN'S HOUSE - BACK PORCH - DAY

Erin, George, and Donna sit on the back porch, lemonades in
hand.

                                        (CONTINUED)

CONTINUED:

                    ERIN
          Donna, I came out instead of calling
          because the judge came up with a number.

                    DONNA
                 (pause)
          A number for the whole group, or for us?

                    ERIN
          Both. He's going to make them pay 333
          million.

Tears of vindication spring to Donna's eyes.

                    DONNA
          Oh my God.

                    ERIN
          And he's making them give five million of
          it to your family.

                    DONNA
          Five million dollars?

                    ERIN
          Five million dollars.

She reels. After a breathless beat:

                    DONNA
          I don't even know how much money that is.

                    ERIN
          Well, it's enough -- it's enough for
          whatever you need, or whatever your girls
          need, or your girls' girls need. It'll be
          enough.

Donna wipes tears off her face.

                    DONNA
          Oh Erin. Oh God.

Donna is overwhelmed. Erin pulls her close.

                    DONNA (cont'd)
          Thank you so much. I don't know what I
          would have done without you.

Erin looks at George over Donna's shoulder, and smiles with
tears in her eyes.

(CONTINUED)

                              ERIN
                    It's a good day.

                              DONNA
                         (laughing and crying)
                    This is too much.

INT. MASRY & VITITOE'S NEW OFFICE BUILDING - DAY

Now this is where the hot lawyers work. A gleaming testament
to power.

INT. MASRY & VITITOE NEW OFFICE - DAY

Boxes everywhere. They just moved in. Everyone is unpacking
at his or her desk. Rosalind is manning the new phones.

                              ROSALIND
                    Masry & Vititoe, can I -- shoot!
                              (she lost them)
                    Masry & Vititoe, can I -- damn it.
                              (calling out)
                    Does anyone know anything about these
                    phones?

INT. ED'S NEW OFFICE - DAY

Ed is in his new office on the phone. In his lap is a copy
of "Los Angeles Lawyer" with his face on the cover.

                              ED
                    Everybody loves the desk you picked out
                    for me, babies. It's great. And guess
                    who's on the cover of Los Angeles Lawyer
                    magazine?

A MESSENGER enters carrying an ENVELOPE.

                              ED
                    Talk to you later, babies. Bye.

He takes the envelope from the Messenger.

                              ED (cont'd)
                    Thank you.

                              MESSENGER
                    You're welcome.

He exits as Ed opens the envelope, revealing what appears to
be a check of some sort. Ed smiles and rises from his desk,
check in hand.

INT. ERIN'S NEW OFFICE - DAY

A spacious, well-designed office with floor-to-ceiling
windows behind Erin's desk. Erin is in the middle of a
conversation.

                    ERIN
               (on phone)
          ...See, I'd much rather walk her through
          this in person because there are some
          things I want to show her, visual aids and
          documents and stuff, so if you could just
          tell her that I won't take up too much of
          her time...
               (listens)
          Right...
               (listens)
          Well, it's a little more complicated than
          Hinkley, so let me do that...

Ed enters, check in hand. Erin exchanges a look with him as
he approaches her desk.

                    ERIN (cont'd)
          ...well, tell her I'm not a lawyer, that
          may help.
               (listens, smiles)
          Great. Why don't you give me the address
          now, just in case...okay.

She writes as Ed waits with a hint of mischievous
expectation.

                    ERIN (cont'd)
          Boy, I would appreciate that so much...You
          are the best!...OK..Huh-uh..All right.
          Thanks so much. Bye.

She hangs up and smiles at Ed from behind her desk.

                    ERIN (cont'd)
          What's up?

                    ED
          I have your bonus check.

                    ERIN
               YAY!

As she reaches up to take it Ed pulls it back slightly, to
explain:

(CONTINUED)

CONTINUED:

                         ED
          Well, Erin, now - I just want you to be
          prepared...It's not exactly the figure we
          discussed.

                         ERIN
                    (loses smile)
          Why not?

                         ED
          Because after very careful consideration,
          I felt that figure was not...appropriate.

As Ed speaks he takes the check out of the envelope and
places it on the the edge of Erin's desk. Erin doesn't even
glance towards it - her eyes are fixed on Ed.

                         ED (cont'd)
          ..and although you may not agree, you're
          going to have to trust that my experience
          and my judgment in these matters.

                         ERIN
                    (pissed)
          Trust! You want me to trust yo-
                    (can't finish)
          Do me a favor, Ed - don't use big words
          you don't understand!

                         ED
          It's a complicated issue, Erin. You're
          not a qualified lawyer...

She rises and begins moving in on the kill.

                         ERIN
          I did a job. You should reward me
          accordingly. It's not complicated, Ed. You
          know what? That's the fucking problem. All
          you lawyers do is complicate situations
          that aren't complicated. You want to know
          why people think lawyers are bloodsucking,
          backstabbing, scumbags - BECAUSE THEY ARE!

                         ED
          Erin -

> ERIN
> I can't believe you're doing this! NOW!
> When I am up to my ass in Kettleman
> plaintiffs - which, by the way, is looking
> like it may be double the amount we had in
> Hinkley - I'm supposed to go out there,
> leave my kids to be raised by strangers,
> knock on doors, get these people to trust
> you with their lives and the whole time
> you're screwing me.

Erin grabs the check off her desk and turns to face Ed;

> ERIN (cont'd)
> And I want you to know something - It
> isn't the number. It's about how my work
> is valued in this firm. It's about how no
> matter what I do, you still treat me like
> I'm not wort--...!!

During her tirade, her eye has caught sight of the figure on
the check. TWO MILLION DOLLARS. Her jaw drops open. She
looks at Ed.

> ED
> As I was saying, I decided the figure you
> proposed was inappropriate. So I
> increased it.

Erin, for the first time, doesn't know what to say.

> ERIN
> Ed, I...I...

Ed is about to leave, but before he does:

> ED
> Do they teach beauty queens to apologize?
> Because you suck at it.

He turns with calm satisfaction and leaves, giving himself a
little cheer. Erin smiles and goes back to work.

                                                    CUT TO:

INT. SUBURBAN HOME - DAY.

We are looking through the doorway of a pretty typical
suburban home. We see Erin pulling up in her Chevy Blazer.

TITLE CARD:

CONTINUED:

The settlement awarded to the plaintiffs in the case of Hinkley vs. PG&E was the largest in a direct-action lawsuit in United States history.

Erin is approaching the doorway.

TITLE CARD:

PG&E claims they no longer uses hexavalent chromium in any of their compressor plants and all of their holding ponds are lined to prevent groundwater contamination.

Erin rings the door bell.

TITLE CARD:

Erin and Ed have seven other cases pending, including one against PG&E regarding a plant in Kettleman Hills, CA.

A housewife answers the door. We stay on Erin, over the housewife's shoulder.

THE END.

STILLS

ERIN BROCKOVICH
Julia Roberts

ED MASRY
Albert Finney

Top: Erin Brockovich *(Julia Roberts)* and Ed Masry *(Albert Finney),* her attorney.
Bottom: Erin Brockovich *(Roberts)* and her next door neighbor and friend George *(Aaron Eckhart).*

Erin Brockovich *(Roberts)*, a worker in a small law firm, whose passion, tenacity, and steadfast desire to fight for the rights of the underdog defied the odds.

Erin Brockovich *(Roberts)*, hired as a file clerk, never gives up searching for the truth about the water system.

Top: Erin Brockovich *(Roberts)*, a single mother with no legal training, joins forces with attorney Ed Masry *(Finney)* and together they win the largest settlement ever paid in a direct-action lawsuit.

Bottom: Erin Brockovich *(Roberts)*, the woman who brought a small town to its feet and a huge company to its knees, at home with her daughter.

Julia Roberts on the set of *Erin Brockovich*.

PRODUCTION NOTES

ERIN BROCKOVICH—MORE THAN A MOVIE

On March 17, 2000, Universal Pictures released a film with a title as unlikely as its real-life heroine. The Jersey Films production *Erin Brockovich*, directed by Steven Soderbergh, written by Susannah Grant and starring Julia Roberts and Albert Finney, received widespread acclaim from critics and audiences around the world, becoming the first film in the new century to gross more than $100 million. And it was equally successful overseas where it was released by Sony Pictures. To date *Erin Brockovich* has grossed $250 million worldwide.

Erin Brockovich has, however, had enormous impact beyond its entertainment value. The true story has taken its place alongside such other acclaimed reality-based features about courageous and enterprising women as *Norma Rae* and *Silkwood*. As Rex Reed commented in the *New York Observer*, "*Erin Brockovich* has a timeliness that surpasses its obvious entertainment value. An excellent film of real substance, with a star performance empowered by unfailing material."

THE STORY AND ITS SOURCE

Erin Brockovich, the film's real-life heroine, has emerged as a living role model for millions of young Americans as she continues to uncover the truth about environmental polluters. She has become a national spokeswoman for the environment, and her efforts have effected environmental policy in Los Angeles and California. For her extraordinary efforts, Brockovich has received many honors, including one from the American Trial Lawyers Association's Civil Justice Foundation. She is, as well, in constant demand as a lecturer, fitting in numerous public appearances around her full-time schedule as a professional legal investigator.

MORE HONORS

Erin Brockovich has also begun amassing honors. In December, the film won the prestigious Environmental Media Award for its influence on popular thinking. And the film was selected, along with the classic *To Kill a Mockingbird*, to be viewed by the United Nations General Assembly.

After winning the largest class-action settlement ever filed against a public utility, attorney Ed Masry and Erin Brockovich (now the firm's director of legal research at Masry and Vititoe) are still fighting on several fronts. They are involved in no less than seven separate suits against major corporations, including another civil action against Pacific Gas & Electric. The law firm of Masry & Vititoe has filed a personal injury case for about 1,500 people who lived near plants owned by PG&E.

The firm is also pursuing methyl tertiary butyl ether (MTBE)-related lawsuits in North Carolina and California. The California case has recently gone to trial in San Francisco.

In recent months Chromium 6, the odorless toxic chemical that affected the citizens of Hinkley, California, has been detected in two dozen San Fernando Valley, California, groundwater wells and 30 of the 80 Valley-area federal groundwater monitoring sites in the U.S. Environmental Protection Agency tests, bringing the crucial concern to millions of Southern California residents. On September 15, 2000, the now-celebrated Erin Brockovich appeared before the Los Angeles City Council and chastised officials for what she called their dismissive attitude toward the chemical threat in local drinking water. The council passed a motion calling for California Governor Gray Davis to sign SB 2127, a bill requiring an accelerated review of chromium-tainted drinking water.

On September 29, Davis signed SB 2127, which has come to be known as "THE ERIN BROCKOVICH BILL." The bill gives the State Department of Health Services until January 2002 to report to the state legislature on the amount of Chromium 6 in the San Fernando Valley water aquifer, which supplies 15 percent of Los Angeles' drinking water.

THE TALENT

Actress. In the title role of *Erin Brockovich*, Julia Roberts delivers a spirited, complex and mature performance that earned her the strongest reviews to date in a career that has included films such as *Pretty Woman* and *Steel Magnolias*, both of which brought her Oscar® nominations, as well as some of the most popular movies of the past decade including *My Best Friend's Wedding, Runaway Bride, Notting Hill, The Pelican Brief* and *Sleeping with the Enemy*.

Supporting Actor. The amazing Albert Finney co-stars as Ed Masry, the attorney who, along with his sharp assistant, helped win the largest class-action settlement in U.S. history. This distinguished British actor of stage and screen boasts four Academy Award® nominations for Best Actor: *Tom Jones, Under the Volcano, Murder on the Orient Express* and *The Dresser*.

Direction. Steven Soderbergh's seamless direction of *Erin Brockovich* reaffirms his position as one of America's finest filmmakers. "A milestone," raved *Los Angeles Times* film critic Kenneth Turan in his review of *Erin Brockovich*. "What Soderbergh can do as well as anyone else is bring restraint, intelligence and subtlety to mainstream material, and what a difference that makes. . . "

    Erin Brockovich confirms the promise he displayed in his assured 1989 film debut, the intimate, character-based drama *sex, lies and videotape*, a film which single-handedly launched the American independent film renaissance. It also enhances his growing reputation as a formidable director of the mainstream material such as *Out of Sight*, starring George Clooney and Jennifer Lopez, based on the novel by Elmore Leonard, as well as his evocative and taut thriller *The Limey*, starring Terence Stamp and Peter Fonda.

Screenplay. The original screenplay by Susannah Grant is, in the words of Chris Hewitt, critic for the Knight-Ridder News Service, "direct, intelligent and witty in a way you wouldn't expect a movie about a class-action lawsuit to be." The acclaimed writer of such recent hit films as *Ever After* and *28 Days* is one of Hollywood's fastest rising screenwriting talents. Grant launched her career in 1992 when she received a Nicholl Fellowship in screenwriting from the Academy of Motion Picture Arts and Sciences, copping her first major writing award in 1995 for the Fox TV series *Party of Five*.

Produced By. "A comedy that's the embodiment of brains and heart" is how *The Wall Street Journal's* film critic Joe Morgenstern described *Erin Brockovich*. The film is based on a compelling concept by executive producer Carla Santos Shamberg and is yet another example of the kind of substantive, cutting-edge entertainment that has become synonymous with Jersey Films, the risk-taking production company headed by Danny De Vito, Michael Shamberg and

Stacey Sher. In the few short years since Jersey Films was founded, the company has produced such high-quality films as *Pulp Fiction, Get Shorty, Man on the Moon, Reality Bites, Gattaca* and Soderbergh's *Out of Sight*.

SNYOPSIS

With no money, no job and no prospects on the horizon, Erin Brockovich (Roberts) is a woman in a tight spot. Following a car accident which is not her fault, Erin finds herself even worse off when her attorney fails to win her any kind of settlement. With nowhere else to turn, Erin pleads with her attorney Ed Masry (Albert Finney) to hire her at his law firm. While working there she stumbles on some medical records misplaced in real estate files. Confused, she begins to question the connection and convinces Ed to allow her to investigate. What she discovers is a cover-up involving contaminated water in a local community, which is causing devastating illnesses among its residents.

Although the local citizens are initially leery, Erin's persistence and the genuine interest in their lives captures their attention and earns their trust. She is helped by her next door neighbor George (Aaron Eckhart), a biker whose friendship and support allow her the time to pursue her cause. Going door to door, she signs up more than 600 plaintiffs. Backed by Ed Masry and a major law firm, Erin succeeds in winning the largest settlement ever paid in a direct-action lawsuit in U.S. history. . . . . $333 million. In triumphing over insurmountable odds, she also gains the confidence to reinvent her life.

Universal Pictures and Columbia Pictures present a Jersey Films production of *Erin Brockovich*, one of the year's most critically acclaimed dramas, starring two-time Academy Award® nominee Julia Roberts (*Notting Hill*), Albert Finney (*The Dresser*) and Aaron Eckhart (*In The Company of Men*). Directed by Steven Soderbergh (*Out of Sight, The Limey*), the film is written by Susannah Grant (*Ever After*) and produced by Danny DeVito, Michael Shamberg and Stacey Sher, partners in Jersey Films (*Man on the Moon, Out of Sight, Get Shorty*). Executive producers are John Hardy, who is making his eighth film with Soderbergh, and Carla Santos Shamberg, who originally brought the project to Jersey Films.

The distinguished production team on *Erin Brockovich* is comprised of: director of photography Ed Lachman (*The Limey*); production designer Phil Messina (art director on *Out of Sight*); Academy Award®-winning editor Anne V. Coates (*Lawrence of Arabia, Out of Sight*); costume designer Jeffrey Kurland

(*Man on the Moon*); and three-time Oscar®-nominated composer Thomas Newman (*American Beauty, The Shawshank Redemption*).

Soderbergh also assembled a stellar supporting cast which includes Peter Coyote (*Patch Adams*) as Kurt Potter, a highly successful lawyer whose firm reluctantly agrees to collaborate on the case; Marg Helgenberger (*China Beach*) as a victim of PG&E's cover-up of the contaminated water; acclaimed stage actress Cherry Jones (*The Cradle Will Rock*) as a local resident whose resistance to joining her neighbors in the lawsuit could end the case before it even begins; and nine-year old Scotty Leavenworth (*The Green Mile*) and Gemmenne De la Peña, who is making her feature film debut, as Matthew and Katie, two of Erin's children.

GETTING STARTED

The best stories sometimes come from the most unlikely places. It was during a visit to her chiropractor that Carla Santos Shamberg first heard the about real-life Erin Brockovich. "I couldn't believe it when my doctor told me about her friend Erin. It seemed incredible that this twice-divorced woman with three young children, who had no money, no resources and no formal education, single-handedly put this case together. I thought she seemed like the perfect role model."

Ms. Shamberg planted the seed of this unlikely Cinderella story with her husband Michael Shamberg, who along with Danny DeVito and Stacey Sher is partnered in Jersey Films. The fact that one woman's passion could have such a positive effect on so many people around her, while at the same time completely transforming her life, seemed the ideal subject matter for the big screen, a gut feeling which has been borne out by the finished product, a high water mark, not only for Jersey Films, but for director Steven Soderbergh and the film's star Julia Roberts.

"Erin is a very warm person and it is that aspect of her character that enabled her to get these families to trust her with intimate stories about their lives," says Ms. Shamberg. "And through the support of Ed Masry, she was allowed to follow her instincts with this case."

At the time Erin and Ed met, the lawyer was winding down his career and was looking forward to retirement. "And then this girl walked in and everything changed," says Ms. Shamberg. In 1993, after Erin and Ed gathered the cooperation of more than 600 plaintiffs, they partnered with a major law firm and went after the powerhouse PG&E, a $30 billion corporation.

As a result of their efforts, PG&E awarded the plaintiffs for $333 million, the largest settlement ever paid in a direct-action lawsuit in U.S. history.

The fact that Erin Brockovich wasn't a lawyer and had no formal education or experience as a law clerk or a paralegal, made her victory that much more memorable, and her tenacity and perseverance has served as an inspirational model.

ASSEMBLING THE TEAM

Julia Roberts was thrilled to play the title character. The actress, whose films have grossed more than $2 billion worldwide, had one of her biggest years in 1999, starring opposite Hugh Grant in Universal's box office smash *Notting Hill* and reteaming with her *Pretty Woman* co-star Richard Gere in *The Runaway Bride*.

Stacey Sher, who along with Shamberg had worked closely with Steven Soderbergh during *Out of Sight*, felt that Soderbergh might be interested in directing this film because "Steven loves stories where what the world sees and what the character sees are two different things. This story is about an extraordinary woman who is really not at all as she appears. Her story is so dramatic and funny and big on its own, that we wanted someone who would keep it grounded and real. There is never anything sentimental or overblown and glossy about Steven's work. We knew he would take this classic story and keep it classic." Michael Shamberg says that "we called Steven and told him he had to read the script and the very next morning he called back and said he wanted to do it."

Soderbergh, whose groundbreaking directorial debut *sex, lies, and videotape* won the Palme d'Or at the Cannes Film Festival and earned him international acclaim, has also directed *Kafka, King of the Hill, The Underneath, Schizopolis, Gray's Anatomy* and the critical hit *Out of Sight*. He followed it up with the well-received crime drama, *The Limey*, starring Terence Stamp and Peter Fonda the following year. In addition to *Erin Brockovich*, this year Soderbergh has directed another innovative drama, *Traffic*.

The attraction of *Erin Brockovich* for Soderbergh was based on its strong, linear screenplay, which "was performance-driven and had a female protagonist who was in every scene in the film. I had never done a film like that before and it really appealed to me."

Before proceeding, Soderbergh carefully researched the true story to make certain that the film honed close to reality. He was aided immeasurably in this effort by screenwriter Susannah Grant. The events depicted in Grant's screenplay are accurate in terms of what really happened as are the central characters, though some of the subsidiary characters are either fictional or composites of real people in Erin's life.

Soderbergh and Grant made a conscious decision to avoid courtroom scenes, opting to instead focus on the step-by-step process by which Erin and Ed went through the case because "this is not really a movie about a lawsuit," Soderbergh says. "It's about a person who cannot seem to reconcile how she views herself with how others view her. Erin is very bright and very quick but she also has a tendency to be very confrontational. She is confrontational in the way she dresses, which is very provocative, and in her language which tends to be very direct, and very colorful."

If Julia Roberts hadn't already been attached to play Erin, says Soderbergh, he would have insisted on her. "It's a role that plays to all of Julia's considerable strengths. There is a certain irrepressibility about her that's riveting. And just like the real Erin there's also something more significant, something darker at the core. They both share an inherent charisma."

Roberts was totally in the thrall of the real Erin Brockovich. "As a person, Erin really intrigues me," Roberts confesses. "I have great admiration for what she stands for. A lot of women in our culture are facing being a single mother, trying to make ends meet. They are the heroes of our time, aren't they?"

Brockovich's self-assurance against daunting obstacles also earned Roberts' admiration and respect. "She is who she is and doesn't change for anybody—which is what makes her such a remarkable individual. She can be in a situation where she's completely out of place and have no awareness of that and just focus on the issue at hand."

Roberts was also drawn to the unique relationship between Erin and Ed Masry. "Ed and Erin bring out the best in each other in an odd-couple kind of way," says Roberts. "He was at a point in his life where he was looking forward to retiring and playing golf. Erin, in stirring up this pot and bringing all of this information to light, re-ignited his passion for justice and you can prevail to make the world a better place to live."

Another potent attraction was that fact Erin's story is ongoing. Not only did she triumph over PG&E in 1996, but she and Ed Masry are currently involved in seven other pending cases, one of which is also against PG&E regarding a plant in Kettleman Hills, California.

"What happened in Hinkley is terrifying, because you think, 'well what else is happening?'" says Roberts. "'Where else are we being deceived?'

The Hinkley residents were so trusting. They felt that they owed so much to this company (PG&E) because they employed most of the town. When they were told that Chromium 6 was good for you, they believed it. Even when they learned what type of chromium was really being used and that it was harmful, it took a lot of convincing for some of them to come around. To think that this company, which was like a parent, had been keeping the truth from them all that time. It's heartbreaking."

British born actor Albert Finney who has graced the stage and screen for more than four decades, amassing four Academy Award® nominations for Best Actor in the process (*Tom Jones, Murder on the Orient Express, Under the Volcano* and *The Dresser*) was selected to play Ed Masry, who is crucial in exposing the water contamination case. "I thought Ed was a fantastic character and the contrast between he and Erin is so hilarious that when we discussed who might play the part, Albert was my first wish," says Soderbergh. "I've always liked and admired his work and he seemed to have exactly the right feel to go with Julia. Just picturing the two of them driving in a car in the desert made me laugh."

Finney was interested from his first read of Susannah Grant's screenplay. "The script was so gripping that I read it in one sitting. Then Steven came to London and we had lunch and I totally enjoyed his company. He seemed relaxed and easy, and admiring of some of the work I've done in film in the past — which immediately makes one warm to a person," he adds with a sly wink.

"It's sad the way these people were treated by a huge corporation," Finney continues. "There's something about it that is worrying. Erin initially is intrigued by medical reports she finds in the files. When she asks Ed if she can look into it, he says 'sure, sure,' just to get her out of the office. She goes off to Hinkley and discovers that people are ill and don't know why. She's the only person at Masry & Vititoe who has met these people personally and it's through her humanity and caring that she gradually builds up a case to which Ed is drawn by her dynamism and enthusiasm, though he knows that a corporation as large as PG&E could bury them in paperwork for years and years. But Erin, through her straightforward arguments, wins him over."

According to Soderbergh, Erin was like the point guard in dealing with all the residents of Hinkley. "The case literally would never have gotten off the ground without her impatience with procedure and her frustration at methods she felt were either not in the immediate interest of the people she was representing or would not be understood by them," he says.

Adding to Finney's enthusiasm for *Erin Brockovich* was the casting of Julia Roberts in the central role. When he first heard she was going to play Erin, "I thought it was a great part for her. Now, after working with her, I have to add that the part is very fortunate to have her playing it. She's terrific, one of those blessed creatures who you like to look at, who you enjoy watching. It's a very sort of magnetic gift."

Aside from the support that the real-life Erin received from Ed Masry, there was another person in her life who made it possible for her to tackle her mammoth workload to move the case forward. George first met Erin when he moved next door to the single mother. It was the late-night revving of his Harley Davidson that caught her attention . . . and not in a positive way. George redeemed himself first by his affection for her children and eventually he and Erin developed a relationship. In casting the role of George, Soderbergh wanted an actor with an unusual combination of character traits. On the one hand, he's a biker and on the other hand he has a very strong desire to be a family man. It was a tough assignment, and one which fell to Aaron Eckhart whom Soderbergh had admired in Neil LaBute's *In the Company of Men*.

The opportunity to play a real person was irresistible, Eckhart says, "because the story can never go off course. You always have a barometer. Because this really happened, the path is already there. This story is invested with real emotions, real lives, real people. When we were filming in Hinkley, we shot right next to the actual PG&E plant that poisoned these people. That's very powerful. We also met some of the families that were involved which made the film so much more important, because this could have happened to anyone of us or to our families."

Roberts enjoyed Eckhart's acting style. "Aaron is such a great actor. On the page, George is a good guy but Aaron has brought him to life in a way that has made him layered and textured. It made my job, as a person who is supposed to love and rely on him, effortless. I knew when I had scenes with Aaron that I just had to listen and go with it."

For producer Danny DeVito, the casting of the film was a producer's dream. "From the very beginning there was a company feeling about this film," he says. "It would have been very easy to make a caricature version of the players in the story, but the entire cast brought extreme reality to the characters. There was this tremendous chemistry between Julia and Aaron and she makes Erin an immensely compassionate and complicated human being. Also, they both have a real ability to retain the whole picture. Actors often just play the moment, but Julia and Aaron, also displayed an uncanny sense of knowing where their characters are heading."

Producer Michael Shamberg feels that much of the same holds true about the film's other central relationship between Finney and Roberts. "Albert and Julia were a great team," Shamberg says. "His Ed is the perfect foil for her character, Erin, and she's the perfect prod for him. The real Erin and Ed are exactly like that in real life."

In speaking of Soderbergh, who never sits at a video monitor, but is usually operating the camera or right beside it, Roberts says, "Steven gave me a great sense of security and confidence. I felt like he was really in there with me. I think he just loves movies and I think that as a filmmaker, he feels a responsibility to make a good film. I love that he runs the camera and is so aware of the precision of our composition and the way things look inside the lens."

"I threw the video assist away about five years ago," states Soderbergh, "because I felt it was making me passive. I had shot all of my own short films and on *The Limey* I began operating again. There really is no substitute for looking through the lens while the performance is happening. The sense of what you are actually getting is very strong. I think for the actors there is a comfort level because they know they're being seen in a way that is absolutely undiluted."

Finney concurs with Roberts' assessment. "Steven is very decisive about when he's got it. He doesn't bumble about thinking 'well have I or haven't I?' I think he believes that if he has cast the film right then the players will be able to do the work. They will just need an occasional nudge in a certain direction. There is a terrific atmosphere on the set. Everyone seems to be having a good time."

Eckhart too, found Soderbergh's presence on the set very comforting. "You can go to him and ask him questions and talk about the film," he says. "He lets the actors be unless there is a problem, which is nice and he always does everything with a smile. He creates an atmosphere where you can be creative and calm. And that's when you can make a good movie."

CAST AND CREW CREDITS

UNIVERSAL PICTURES AND COLUMBIA PICTURES PRESENT

A JERSEY FILMS PRODUCTION

JULIA ROBERTS

ERIN BROCKOVICH

ALBERT FINNEY   AARON ECKHART

MARG HELGENBERGER   CHERRY JONES

VEANNE COX   CONCHATA FERRELL   TRACEY WALTER

CASTING BY MARGERY SIMKIN

MUSIC BY THOMAS NEWMAN

MUSIC SUPERVISOR AMANDA SCHEER-DEMME

COSTUME DESIGN BY JEFFREY KURLAND

EDITED BY ANNE V. COATES, A.C.E.

PRODUCTION DESIGN BY PHILIP MESSINA

PHOTOGRAPHED BY ED LACHMAN, A.S.C.

CO-PRODUCER GAIL LYON

EXECUTIVE PRODUCERS JOHN HARDY   CARLA SANTOS SHAMBERG

PRODUCED BY DANNY DEVITO   MICHAEL SHAMBERG   STACEY SHER

WRITTEN BY SUSANNAH GRANT

DIRECTED BY STEVEN SODERBERGH

CAST

(In Order of Appearance)

Erin Brockovich	JULIA ROBERTS
Dr. Jaffe	DAVID BRISBIN
Rosalind	DAWN DIDAWICK
Ed Masry	ALBERT FINNEY
Donald	VALENTE RODRIGUEZ
Brenda	CONCHATA FERRELL
Los Angeles Judge	GEORGE ROCKY SULLIVAN
Defending Lawyer	PAT SKIPPER
Defendant	JACK GILL
Mrs. Morales	IRENE OLGA LÓPEZ
Beth (8 months)	EMILY MARKS
	JULIE MARKS
Matthew	SCOTTY LEAVENWORTH
Katie	GEMMENNE DE LA PEÑA
Waitress	ERIN BROCKOVICH-ELLIS
Anna	ADILAH BARNES
Babysitter	IRINA V. PASSMOORE
George	AARON ECKHART
Biker Friends	RON ALTOMARE
	CHARLES JOHN BUKEY
Donna Jensen	MARG HELGENBERGER
Brian Frankel	RANDY LOWELL
Scott	JAMIE HARROLD
Ashley Jensen	SARAH ASHLEY
Shanna Jensen	SCARLETT POMERS
David Foil	T.J. THYNE
Tom Robinson	JOE CHREST
Mandy Robinson	MEREDITH ZINNER
Pete Jensen	MICHAEL HARNEY
Bob Linwood	WILLIAM LUCKING
Laura Ambrosino	MIMI KENNEDY

Mike Ambrosino . . . . SCOTT SOWERS	GARY BREWER
Pamela Duncan . . . . CHERRY JONES	GLENN M. CARRERE
Annabelle Daniels . . . . KRISTINA MALOTA	CHERYL GOULD
Ted Daniels . . . . WADE ANDREW WILLIAMS	JENNIFER LAGURA
Rita Daniels . . . . CORDELIA RICHARDS	On-Set Dresser . . . . MIKE MALONE
Beth (18 months) . . . . ASHLEY PIMENTAL	
BRITTANY PIMENTAL	A Camera Second Assistant . . . . MARTA E. WEISS
Charles Embry . . . . TRACEY WALTER	B Camera Second Assistant . . . . . . ISAAC FRIEDMAN
Nelson Perez . . . . LARRY MARTINEZ	Camera Loader . . . . STACY DE LA MOTTE
Judge LeRoy A. Simmons . . . . HIMSELF	Location Projectionists . . . . TOMMY DICKSON
PG&E Lawyers . . . . DON SNELL	E.J. BUTCH ERTEL
MICHAEL SHAMBERG	
Ms. Sanchez . . . . GINA GALLEGO	Lighting Consultant . . . . JOHN W. DE BLAU
Kurt Potter . . . . PETER COYOTE	Gaffer . . . . RUSSELL CALDWELL
Car Messenger . . . . RONALD E. HAIRSTON	Best Boy Electric . . . . FRANK ENDEWARDT
Theresa Dallavale . . . . VEANNE COX	Electricians . . . . GARY M. LANG
Town Meeting Plaintiff . . . . SCOTT ALLEN	DARRYL MURCHISON
Ruth Linwood . . . . SHEILA SHAW	JOHN OWENS
Bartender . . . . MATTHEW KIMBROUGH	DAVID WATSON
Check Messenger . . . . JASON CERVANTES	Rigging Gaffer . . . . RICHARD HARTLEY
Stunt Coordinator . . . . JOHN ROBOTHAM	Best Boy Rigging . . . . DAVE TUTOKEY
Stunt Doubles . . . . TABBY HANSON	Rigging Electrician	KEITH HARTLEY
ROYDON CLARK	
Unit Production Manager . . . . . . FREDERIC W. BROST	Key Grip . . . . CHARLES BUKEY
First Assistant Director . . . . GREGORY JACOBS	Best Boy Grip . . . . RODNEY VETO
Second Assistant Director . . . . DAVE HALLINAN	Dolly Grip . . . . PAUL THRELKELD
Set Decorator . . . . KRISTEN TOSCANO MESSINA	Grips . . . . THOMAS A. CURRAN
	WAYNE L. DUNCAN
A Camera Operator . . . . CRIS LOMBARDI	DICE MIYAKE
A Camera First Assistant . . . . BARRY IDOINE	Rigging Key Grip . . . . MARK R. SHULTZ
B Camera First Assistant . . . . BOB BROWN	Rigging Grips . . . . RANDY BERRETT
	ANTHONY PORTO
Production Sound Mixer . . . . THOMAS CAUSEY	PAUL E. SUTTON
Boom Operator . . . . JOE BRENNAN	PAUL D. WILLIAMS
Utility Sound . . . . RICHARD KITE	
	2nd 2nd Assistant Director . . . . MICHAEL RISOLI
Production Coordinator . . . . . . ROBIN L. LE CHANU	Set Production Assistants . . . . KERI BRUNO
Production Accountant . . . . RICKI L. STEIN	MICHAEL LA CORTE
Script Supervisor . . . . ANNIE WELLES	LUKE POLLOCK
	LYNN STRUIKSMA
Art Director . . . . CHRISTA MUNRO	DGA Trainee . . . . TONY ENG
Assistant Art Director . . . . . . KEITH P. CUNNINGHAM	
Set Designers . . . . MASAKO MASUDA	First Assistant Editor . . . . ROBB SULLIVAN
PATRICIA KLAWONN	Avid Assistant Editor . . . . JOHN AXELRAD
Property Master . . . . PETER BANKINS	Second Assistant Editor . . . . BRAD DEAN
Assistant Property Master . . . . . ALBERTO CHRISTIANO	Apprentice Editor . . . . JULIAN ANDRAUS
LOMBARDO	Editorial Intern . . . . GLENN ARCARO
Property Assistant . . . . ROBERT BANKINS	
Art Department Coordinator . . . . . . BLAIR HUIZINGH	Special Effects by . . . . KEVIN HANNIGAN
Art Department Assistant . . . . SARAH BULLION	Special Effects Foremen . . . . WILLIAM HARRISON
Buyer . . . . STACY WEDDINGTON	KENNETH J. VAN ORDER
Leadmen . . . . SCOTT A. BOBBITT	Special Effects Assistant . . . . WERNER HAHNLEIN
JASON BEDIG	
Set Dressers . . . . DALE E. ANDERSON	Costume Supervisor . . . . ELENA DEL RIO
BART BARBUSCIA	Key Costumers . . . . JANIS MEKAELIAN
BRENT BLOM	RHONA MEYERS
	TOM SIEGAL

Set Costumer for Julia Roberts . . . . FRANCIS VEGA
Set Costumers . . . . COREY C. BRONSON
                       SHOSHANA RUBIN
                       EMILY WYSS

Julia Roberts' Makeup by . . . . RICHARD DEAN
Key Makeup Artist . . . . SUSAN CABRAL-EBERT
Additional Makeup . . . . NORMAN PAGE
Tattoo Designer . . . . KEN DIAZ

Julia Roberts' Hair Designs by . . . . BONNIE CLEVERING
Hair Department Head . . DEBORAH MILLS-WHITLOCK
Hair Stylists . . . . MICHELLE WEISS
                       BERNARD GOUGH
                       ANTHONY WILSON

Location Manager . . . . KEN LAVET
Assistant Location Managers . . . . JANE E. GRAVES
. . . . QUENTIN HALLIDAY
Location Production Assistant . . . . . . P. CALEB DUFFY

First Assistant Accountant . . . . CHERI HALL
Assistant Accountants . . . . GAVIN J. BEHRMAN
                       RICHARD E. CASTRO
                       LAURA TIZ
Construction Auditor. . . . . MIRASOL JIMENEZ
Accounting Clerk . . . . JIM SCHIRO

Production Supervisor . . . . JAMES C. TAYLOR
Assistant Production Coordinators . . . KAREN JARNECKE
. . . . NANCY REID
Production Secretary . . . . J. LARSEN JAY
Office Production Assistants. . . . . JAMES BADSTIBNER
                       CLELIO BOCCATO
                       CHERIE SUPNE
                       PATRICK THORNHILL
                       DENISE N. LEWIS
                       GRANT A. PASLEY
Studio Teacher. . . . . THOMAS J. MCGOWAN
Production Intern. . . . . TAINA MIRACH

Casting Associate . . . . CARMEN CUBA
. . . .
Extras Casting . . . . RICH KING
                       JAY KRYMIS
Casting Intern . . . . GINA STAINBROOK

Unit Publicist . . . . SPOOKY STEVENS
Still Photographer. . . . . BOB MARSHAK
Assistant to Mr. Soderbergh & Mr. Hardy. . . . . . CAITLIN
  MALONEY
Assistant to Mr. DeVito . . . . LAURIE RECORD
Assistant to Mr. Shamberg . . . . DAMON BINGHAM
Assistant to Ms. Sher. . . . . SINDY LIN
Assistant to Ms. Sher & Mr. Shamberg. . . NATASHA CUBA
Assistant to Ms. Shamberg . . . . . JENNIFER FUKASAWA
Assistant to Ms. Lyon . . . . AMY PELTONEN

Assistant to Mr. Finney . . . . JOHN O. FALVEY
Assistant to Ms. Roberts . . . . BRAD FURMAN
Cast Assistants . . . . BRUMBY J. BROUSSARD
                       RICH EPSTEIN
Dialect Coach for Mr. Finney. . . . . . . CARLA MEYER
Stand-Ins . . . . JULIE WAGNER
                       MARC C. GESCHWIND

Security for Ms. Roberts . . . . SISS LTD.
                       JOSEPH KEIDETH
                       BRADLEY STEYN
Construction Coordinator . . . . CHRIS SNYDER
General Foreman. . . . . WILLIAM W. GIDEON
Plaster Foremen . . . . ADAM BARKER
                       TRACY W. STOCKWELL
Location Foreman . . . . GERARD FORREST
Labor Foremen. . . . . LOUIE ESPARZA
                       BOB FIDALGO
                       ANTHONY J. SAENZ, JR.
Propmaker Foremen . . . . JOHN BULLARD
                       JOHN MOORE
                       ROBERT NICKLOFF
                       JAMES PANIAGUA
                       DALE SNYDER
Paint Supervisor . . . . HANK GIARDINA
Standby Painter . . . . FRANK LUCKY COSTELLO
Paint Foremen . . . . STEVEN J. KERLAGON
                       CRAIG T. SHORDON
                       DAVID CLARK
Painter Gangboss . . . . SCOTT SHORDON
Painter . . . . BRUCE SMITH
Welding Foreman . . . . BUD KUCIA
Greensmen . . . . RICHARD BORIS
                       ANDREW KNOWLAND

Propmakers . . . . BILL DUFFIN
                       MICHAEL JON DUFFIN
                       LOUIE ESPARZA, JR.
                       STEPHEN A. GINDORF
                       BRIAN D. GRAY
                       KAREN KORNBAU
                       DEVLIN LEREW
                       LOREN NICKLOFF
                       STEVE WILLIS
                       CURTIS A. YAKEL

Laborers . . . . MICHAEL A. CONTRERAZ
                       EDDIE ESPARZA
                       ARTHUR G. LOPEZ
                       ERNIE L. MENCHACA, JR.
                       EDMUND A. PANIAGUA
                       GEORGE E. VIELMA

Transportation Coordinator . . . . JON CARPENTER
Transportation Captain. . . . . SHANE GREEDY

Transportation Co-Captain . . . . RICH BENNETTI	Post-Production Assistant . . . . MONICA DE ARMOND
Camera Car Drivers . . . . JACK CARPENTER	Post-Production Accountant . . . . LEAH HOLMES
BYRON CARTER	
Insert Car Driver . . . . J. ARMIN GARZA II	Dialogue Editor . . . . AARON GLASCOCK
	Assistant Sound Editor . . . . JAMES MORIOKA
Drivers . . . . LOREN BESS	Sound Effects Recording . . . . ERIC POTTER
PAT CARMAN	
GARY CHEEK	Additional Sound Editors . . . . JULIE FEINER
MARTIN COBLENZ	MICHAEL CHOCK
LOUIS DINSON	MARVIN WALOWITZ
RONALD B. DINSON	DAVID A. WHITTAKER
GUY DUQUETTE	Foley Editor . . . . EZRA DWECK
CHARLES ENZEN	Additional Assistant Sound Editor . . . BAYLIS GLASCOCK
SCOTT FAIR	Post-Production Sound Services . . . . . . WEDDINGTON
BERNARD GLAVIN	PRODUCTIONS
DAVID L. GLAVIN	
DIANE GLAVIN	Foley by . . . . ALICIA IRWIN
LEON L. GLAVIN	DAWN FINTOR
CHRIS GORDEN	Foley Mixer . . . . DAVID BETANCOURT
BILLY GRACE	Foley Recordist . . . . JON VOGL
DONALD S. HARBACK	Voice Casting . . . . L.A. MADDOGS
MIKE HUTMACHER	
DAVID T. JERNIGAN	Re-Recorded at . SOUNDELUX VINE STREET STUDIOS
JAMES E. JOHNSON	Recordist . . . . ERIC FLICKINGER
POPS JOHNSON	Engineering . . . . PAT STOLTZ
THOMAS M. KRIGBAUM	
J.T. LANNEN	Music Supervisor . . . . . . AMANDA SCHEER-DEMME
HAL LARY	Music Consultant . . . . BUCK DAMON
KEN MERRITT	
TOM NEAL	Music Editor . . . . BILL BERNSTEIN
DON R. NEWTON	Assistant Music Editor . . . . JORDAN CORNGOLD
JOHN P. ORNSTEIN	Music Scoring Mixer . . . . DENNIS S. SANDS
CURTIS RANDOLL	Recordists . . . . TOM HARDISTY
CHANCE ROBERTSON	DAVID MARQUETTE
ALBERT C. RUSK, JR.	Orchestrator . . . . THOMAS PASATIERI
TED SCHAMBERS	Music Contractor . . . . LESLIE MORRIS
CLINTON TAYLOR	Music Preparation . . . . JULIAN BRATOLYUBOV
RAYMOND VAN HOLTEN	Music Recorded at . . . . . TODD-AO SCORING STAGE
KELLY YON	Music Recorded & Mixed at . . . . SIGNET SOUNDELUX
Set Medics . . . . KERI LITTLEDEER	Digital Visual Effects by . . . . CINESITE, INC.
HAROLD FOWLER	Visual Effects Supervisor . . . . TOM SMITH
GORDON GREER	Visual Effects Producer . . . . CAROLE COWLEY
Construction Medic . . . . SAM COBB	Digital Compositors . . . . TOM ZILS
Set Security . . . . JOHN RAMIREZ	MARK TAIT LEWIS
Caterer . . . . GOURMET ON LOCATION, INC.	JASON PICCIONI
Chef . . . . CHEF ANTOINE MASCARO	Paint Supervisor . . . . CORRINE POOLER
Craft Service . . . . RONALD E. HAIRSTON	Digital Artist . . . . SERENA NARAMORE
CHARLES DRAKE	
Supervising Sound Editor . . . . LARRY BLAKE	Titles & Opticals . . . . HOWARD ANDERSON CO.
Re-Recording Mixers . . . . LARRY BLAKE	Negative Cutter . . . . GARY BURRITT
MICHAEL KELLER, C.A.S.	Color Timer . . . . DANA ROSS
	Dailies Telecine / Track Negative . . . . NT AUDIO VIDEO
	FILM LABS
	Cutting Continuity . . . . MASTERWORDS
Post-Production Supervisor . . . . . . CAITLIN MALONEY	Camera Dollies by . . . . CHAPMAN / LEONARD

"Redemption Day"
Performed by Sheryl Crow
Written by Sheryl Crow
Courtesy of A&M Records
Under license from Universal Music Enterprises

"Bluegrass Hoedown"
Written & Performed by Chris Horvath
Courtesy of Del Rey Music, Inc./Who Did That Music? Library

"Honey Bunch"
Written by Paul Kerr & Andy Dewar
Courtesy of Opus 1

"Two Shots Of Rye"
Written by Paul Kerr & Andy Dewar
Courtesy of Opus 1

"Everyday Is A Winding Road"
Performed by Sheryl Crow
Written by Sheryl Crow, Brian MacLeod, Jeff Trott
Courtesy of A&M Records
Under license from Universal Music Enterprises

"The Young And The Restless" and "Wheel Of Fortune"
Courtesy of Columbia TriStar Television

The Los Angeles Times © 1999. Reprinted by permission.

Special Thanks to
PAMELA DUMOND
NIKKI ALLYN GROSSO
THOMAS V. GIRARDI, ESQ.
WALTER J. LACK, ESQ.
CHRIS LORD-ALGE

Camera System by CLAIRMONT
COLOR BY CFI
KODAK Motion Picture Film
Digital DTS Sound In Selected Theatres
SDDS In Selected Theatres
8 Channels
Dolby Digital In Selected Theatres
In Selected Theatres
This Film Was Re-Recorded in a Swelltone Theater